Laboratory Experiments for

Advanced Placement Chemistry

Student Edition

Sally Ann Vonderbrink, Ph.D.
Retired Chemistry Teacher
St. Xavier High School
Cincinnati, Ohio

Published By:

Flinn Scientific, Inc.
P.O. Box 219
Batavia, IL 60510

Reference materials taken from the *Flinn Chemical & Biological Catalog/Reference Manual* have been used in Laboratory Experiments for Advanced Placement Chemistry. These reference materials are ©2001, Flinn Scientific, Inc. All Rights Reserved. Reproduction for one-time use with permission from Flinn Scientific, Inc. Batavia, IL USA has been granted to the author. No part of this material may be reproduced or transmitted in any form or by any means, electronic or mechanical, including, but not limited to photocopy, recording, or any information storage and retrieval system, without permission in writing from Flinn Scientific, Inc.

This book is dedicated to
the memory of

Florence F. Vonderbrink

and to

Susan Vonderbrink Quirk

Without their constant encouragement and support
it never would have happened.

Thanks are extended
to the administration of
St. Xavier High School
for a sabbatical
during which much of the writing
was accomplished and to the
students of the
Advanced Placement Chemistry Classes
who cheerfully tested
the experiments.

Thanks are also extended to
Rosemary L. Centner
for carefully proofreading the manuscript.

Table of Contents

General Information

Experiments   Page

Safety in the Laboratory

The chemistry laboratory must be a safe place in which to work and learn about chemistry. In order to be sure that it is safe, there are certain safety rules that must be followed. Most of these involve just using common sense. Be sure to know and to follow all the safety rules.

1. Wear chemical splash goggles at all times while you are in the laboratory. They must be worn to cover your eyes.

2. Wear a chemical-resistant apron.

3. Wash acid, base, or any chemical spill off of yourself immediately with large amounts of water. Notify your teacher of the spill.

4. If chemical substances get in your eye, wash the eye out for 15 minutes. Hold your eye open with your fingers while washing it out.

5. Observe the safety alerts in the laboratory directions.

6. Tie long hair back so it cannot catch fire from a Bunsen burner flame. Hair burns very readily.

7. Wear shoes in the laboratory. Do not wear bulky clothing.

8. Never eat or drink in the laboratory. Don't chew on the end of a pen which was lying on the lab bench.

9. Lubricate glass tubing with glycerol or detergent before putting it into rubber stoppers. Wrap the tubing in a towel, and hold it close to the stopper while gently twisting and inserting it. Never force it.

10. If you take more of a chemical substance from a container than you need, you should not return the excess to the container. This might cause contamination of the substance remaining. Dispose of the excess as your teacher directs.

11. Never smell anything in the laboratory unless your teacher tells you it is safe. Do not smell a substance by putting your nose directly over the container and inhaling. Instead, waft the vapors toward your nose by gently fanning the vapors toward yourself.

12. Never taste materials in the laboratory.

13. Never work in a laboratory alone.

14. Know the location of and the method of operation of safety equipment: fire extinguishers, safety shower, eye wash, safety blanket, fume hood, emergency gas cut-off.

15. If you burn yourself on a hot object, immediately hold the burned area under cold water for 15 minutes. Inform your teacher.

16. Keep the laboratory desk, sink, storage areas, and floor clean, dry and neat.

17. Put lids or caps back on bottles and jars.

18. Clean up spills immediately. If you spill a very reactive substance such as an acid or base, notify the people in the area and then obtain assistance from your teacher. Acid spills should be neutralized with baking soda, base spills with vinegar before cleaning them up.

19. Never heat a closed system.

20. Be sure you have lighted a match before turning on your Bunsen burner.

21. If your Bunsen burner goes out, turn the gas off immediately.

22. When heating a test tube, never point the open end at anyone.

23. Always add acid to water and stir the solution while adding the acid. Never add water to an acid.

24. Report all accidents to your teacher.

25. Clean up broken glass with a brush and dust pan. Do not use your fingers.

26. Dispose of broken glass in the specified container. Do not mix glass with other waste.

27. Absolutely no horseplay is allowed in the laboratory.

The Laboratory Notebook

A laboratory notebook should be used to explain laboratory procedures, record all laboratory data, show how calculations are made, discuss the results of an experiment, and to explain the theories involved.

A record of laboratory work is an important document which will show the quality of the laboratory work that you have done. You may need to show your notebook to the Chemistry Department at a college or university in order to obtain credit for the laboratory part of your Advanced Placement Chemistry course. As you record information in your notebook, keep in mind that someone who is unfamiliar with your work may be using this notebook to evaluate your laboratory experience in chemistry. When you explain your work, list your data, calculate values and answer questions, be sure that the meaning will be obvious to anyone who reads your notebook.

Procedure

1. Use a quadrille-lined book with pages fastened in place.

2. Write your name and class on the front cover and inside the front cover.

3. In ink, number all the right-hand pages on the lower right corner if they are not already numbered. If you are left-handed, you may use the left pages instead of the right if you wish.

4. Save the first two pages for a Table of Contents. This should be kept current as you proceed. Each time you write up a lab, place the title and page number where the lab report begins in the Table of Contents.

5. Write in ink. Use only the right hand pages. You may use the left-hand pages for preliminary notes or for a quick graph. The left-hand pages will not be graded.

6. If you make a mistake DO NOT ERASE. Just draw ONE LINE through your error, and continue. It is expected that some errors will occur. You cannot produce a perfect, error-free notebook. Errors should be corrected by drawing one line through the mistake, and then proceeding with the new data.

7. Do not use the first person or include personal comments.

Laboratory Reports

Include the following information in your laboratory reports:

1. **Title**

   The title should be descriptive. Experiment 5 is not a descriptive title.

2. **Date**

   This is the date (or dates) you performed the experiment.

3. **Purpose**

   A brief statement of what you are attempting to do.

4. **Procedure**

   A one- or two-sentence description of the method you are using. You may refer to the lab manual for specific instructions, but you should include a brief statement of the method. Do not include lengthy, detailed directions. A person who understands chemistry should be able to read this section and know what you are doing.

5. **Data**

   Record all your data directly in your lab notebook on the right-hand pages. Organize your data in a neat, orderly form. Label all data very clearly. Use correct significant digits, and always include proper units (g, mL, etc.). Underline, use capital letters, or use any device you choose to help organize this section well. Space things out—don't try to cram everything on one page. Use tables where appropriate.

6. **Calculations and Graphs**

   You should show *how* calculations are carried out. Give the equation used and show how your values are substituted into it. Give the calculated values. If graphs are included, make the graphs an appropriate size. Label all axes and give each graph a title. See the section on graphing on page viii. If experiments are not quantitative, this section may be omitted.

7. **Conclusions**

   Make a simple statement concerning what you can conclude from the experiment.

8. **Discussion of Theory**

   In this section you should include such information as: What theory was demonstrated in this experiment? What do the calculations show? How was the purpose of the experiment fulfilled? Why does (or doesn't) the experiment work? Refer back to the purpose of the lab to write this section.

9. **Experimental Sources of Error**

   What are some *specific* sources of error, and how do they influence the data? Do they make the values obtained larger or smaller than they should be? Which measurement was the least precise? Instrumental error and human error exist in all experiments, and should not be mentioned as a source of error unless they cause a significant fault. Significant digits and mistakes in calculations are NOT a valid source of error. In writing this section it is sometimes helpful to ask yourself what you would do differently if you were to repeat the experiment and wanted to obtain better precision. If you can calculate a percent error or percent deviation, do so and include it in this section.

10. **Questions**

    Answer any questions included in the lab directions. Answer in such a way that the meaning of the question is obvious from your answer.

Reporting Laboratory Data

Graphing Experimental Data

1. All graphs should have a descriptive title ("Graph" is not a title).

2. Both the vertical and horizontal axes should have labels and units clearly marked. Use a ruler to draw the axes.

3. The scales chosen should reflect the precision of the measurements. For example, if temperature is known to be ±0.1°C, you should be able to plot the value this closely. Don't have each block of the graph equal to 10°C. You may need to use graph paper with smaller divisions than that in the laboratory notebook.

4. There should be a table in which the data values are listed. Don't put data in a graph unless you have first listed it in a table.

5. The controlled or independent variable is conventionally placed on the horizontal axis. The dependent variable is graphed on the vertical axis.

6. There should be an obvious small point on the graph for each experimental value. It is not necessary to include the coordinates of each point since they will be in the data table.

7. A smooth line should be drawn that lies as close as possible to most of the points. Do NOT draw a line connecting one point to the next one as in a dot-to-dot drawing. If the line is a straight line, use a ruler to draw it.

8. If a computer program is used to draw the graph, the rules still apply.

Uncertainty

Every experimental value has some uncertainty associated with it. The amount of uncertainty depends on two things: the precision of the instrument used to make a measurement, and the skill of the person using the instrument.

Plus-or-Minus Notation

The uncertainty of a measurement can be expressed using plus-or-minus notation. For example, an object whose mass is determined on a centigram balance may be found to have a mass of 3.40 ±0.01 gram. The same object, when measured on an analytical balance, may have a mass of 3.4124 ±0.0001 g. The plus-or-minus notation reflects the precision of the balance used for making the measurement.

Significant Digits

Often, the plus-or-minus notation is not used when reporting a measured value. Instead, the significant digit notation is used. When properly assigning significant digits, include all measured digits that are known with certainty and one digit that is an estimate. In the above examples, the mass of the object on the centigram balance should be reported as 3.40 g, and on the analytical balance as 3.4124 g. The last digit in both measurements has some uncertainty. Notice that a final zero is included in the value 3.40 g because this was a measured number. Use the rules for addition, subtraction, multiplication and division of values with significant digits in carrying out your calculations.

Accuracy

Accuracy is a measure of how close an experimental value is to a value which is accepted as correct. The measure of the accuracy of an experimental value is reported as Absolute Error or Percent Error.

Absolute error is just the difference between the measured and accepted values:

Absolute error = Experimental value – Accepted value

Percent error or Relative error is calculated as follows:

$$\% \text{ error} = \frac{\text{Experimental value} - \text{Accepted value}}{\text{Accepted value}} \times 100\%$$

Notice that the error is a positive number if the experimental value is too high, and is a negative number if the experimental value is too low.

Precision

Frequently in science, an accepted or true value is not known. The accuracy of a measurement cannot be reported if an accepted value is unavailable. Since scientists don't know how close they are to the true value, they repeat their experiments several times and report on how close together their values lie. It is hoped that an experiment that can give reproducible results will also give accurate results. Certainly, if data cannot be reproduced, it cannot be reliable.

Precision is a measure of how reproducible experimental measurements are. Precision is reported as Deviation or Difference of values.

The Absolute Deviation or Absolute Difference of each measurement is the difference of each measurement from the mean or average:

Absolute deviation = |Measured value – Mean|

The Average Deviation or Average Difference is the average of all of the absolute deviations.

The Percent Deviation or Percent Difference is the average deviation reported as a percentage:

$$\text{Percent Deviation} = \frac{\text{Average Deviation}}{\text{Mean}} \times 100\%$$

For example, antacid tablets were analyzed to find the amount of sodium carbonate present. The experiment was carried out three times, and the following values were found:

Trial 1   1.69 g

Trial 2   1.74 g

Trial 3   1.68 g

The Mean or Average of the values is:

$$\text{Mean} = \frac{1.69 + 1.74 + 1.68}{3} = 1.70 \text{ g}$$

The Absolute Deviation of each value from the mean is:

Trial 1 $|1.69 - 1.70| = 0.01$ g

Trial 2 $|1.74 - 1.70| = 0.04$ g

Trial 3 $|1.68 - 1.70| = 0.02$ g

The Average Deviation is:

$$\text{Average Deviation} = \frac{0.01 + 0.04 + 0.02}{3} = 0.02 \text{ g}$$

The Relative Deviation or Relative Difference is:

$$\text{Relative Deviation} = \frac{\text{Average Deviation}}{\text{Mean}} \times 100\%$$

$$\text{Relative Deviation} = \frac{0.02}{1.70} \times 100\% = 1.2\%$$

This tells the scientist that on the average, the experiment will give values that are within 1.2% of the average (and hopefully true) value.

Analysis of Silver in an Alloy

In this experiment an alloy of silver is analyzed to determine its silver content. The mass of the silver–copper alloy is measured. The alloy is then dissolved in nitric acid, the silver is precipitated as silver chloride, and the silver chloride is filtered, washed, dried and its mass determined. From the mass of the silver chloride formed and the mass of the original sample, the percent of silver in the alloy can be calculated. Because the results are based on the mass of a product, this procedure is classified as a gravimetric analysis.

Silver and copper are very non-reactive metals. Neither will dissolve in hydrochloric acid or sulfuric acid. The "oxidizing" acid, nitric acid (HNO_3), is required. In acidic solutions the nitrate ion (NO_3^-) is an excellent oxidizer, and it will oxidize $Ag(s)$ to $Ag^+(aq)$ and $Cu(s)$ to $Cu^{2+}(aq)$. The reduction product is the gas nitrogen monoxide (NO). As the colorless nitrogen monoxide gas forms, it immediately reacts with the oxygen in the air to produce the orange-brown gas nitrogen dioxide (NO_2). The half-reactions are as follows:

$$Ag(s) \rightarrow Ag^+(aq) + e^-$$

$$Cu(s) \rightarrow Cu^{2+}(aq) + 2\ e^-$$

$$4\ H^+(aq) + NO_3^-(aq) + 3e^- \rightarrow NO(g) + 2\ H_2O(l)$$

Once the silver and copper are in solution, they can be separated from each other by precipitating the silver as silver chloride. Silver chloride (AgCl) is very insoluble in water, while copper (II) chloride ($CuCl_2$) is soluble. Therefore, addition of chloride ions to the solution will precipitate essentially all of the silver and none of the copper. The silver chloride precipitate is filtered from the solution, dried, and its mass determined.

Chemicals

Silver–copper alloy

Baking Soda, $NaHCO_3(s)$

Nitric acid, HNO_3, 6 M

Sodium chloride, NaCl(s)

Equipment

Beakers, 100- and 250-mL

Stirring rod

Watch glass

Ring stand, ring, wire gauze

Graduated cylinder

Drying oven

Balance, sensitive

Gooch crucible and fiber glass pad, or sintered glass filter crucible

Filter flask and Walter's adapter

Wash bottle

Crucible tongs

Bunsen burner (or hot plate)

Rubber or plastic policeman

Fume hood

Parafilm® or plastic wrap

Procedure

1. Prepare a Filter Crucible.

To filter the solution, either a Gooch crucible or a sintered glass filter crucible will be used with a filter flask. Refer to Figure 1 below to see how the crucible, Walter's adapter, and filter flask are assembled.

If you use a Gooch crucible, clean it, place a fiber glass filter pad in the crucible and pull distilled water through the assembly to be sure the filter pad is seated tightly on the bottom of the crucible. If you are using a filter crucible, clean it and rinse it with distilled water using suction. Place the Gooch or sintered glass filter crucible in a clean beaker and dry it in an oven at 110 °C. When the crucible is dry, *cool it,* and determine its mass using a sensitive balance. Be careful to handle the crucible so that no fingerprints will be present.

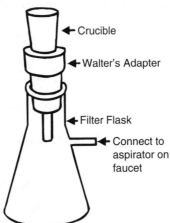

Figure 1. Filter flask with crucible and adapter

2. Find the Mass of the Alloy.

Obtain a sample of silver alloy that is between 0.1 and 0.5 g. Determine its mass precisely on a sensitive balance.

3. Dissolve the Silver.

Put the alloy in a clean 100-mL beaker, and *carefully* pour 10 mL of 6 M nitric acid over it. Cover the beaker with a watch glass so none of the solution spatters out. It may be necessary to gently heat the solution so that the alloy dissolves. Allow the alloy to totally dissolve.

4. Precipitate the Silver.

Calculate the amount of sodium chloride that would be necessary to precipitate the silver in your sample, assuming that the sample is 100% silver. Use a balance sensitive to ±0.01 g to weigh out *two times* this amount of sodium chloride. Dissolve the sodium chloride in 25 mL of distilled water. Remove the watch glass from the first beaker, and rinse any moisture on the bottom of the watch glass back into the beaker with your wash bottle to be sure that no silver is lost. To precipitate the silver as silver chloride, slowly add the sodium chloride solution to the dissolved silver. Stir with a stirring rod, and use distilled water to rinse any solution clinging to the rod back into the beaker. Gently heat (without boiling) the solution for about 15 minutes. This will cause the precipitate particles to grow larger so they are easier to filter. Alternatively, cover the beaker with Parafilm® or plastic wrap and allow it to stand overnight. This will also allow the particles to grow larger.

5. Filter the Silver Chloride.

Attach the filter crucible to a suction flask. Pour some distilled water through the filter with suction to be sure that the filter pad firmly seals the bottom of the Gooch crucible. In your wash bottle, add 2 mL of 6 M HNO_3 to 150 mL of distilled water. Label your wash bottle appropriately. Use this as a rinse. The addition of the acid to the rinse water helps to keep the precipitate from "peptizing," or forming extremely small particles that will run through the filter. Carefully pour the solution above the silver chloride down a stirring rod into the crucible. Wash the precipitate into the crucible with the diluted nitric acid solution. Be sure to get every particle! A rubber policeman on a stirring rod can be used as a squeegee to clean the sides of the beaker. Rinse the precipitate several times with the wash solution.

6. Dry the Silver Chloride and Determine Its Mass.

Put the crucible with silver chloride in a clean beaker, cover it with a watch glass, and let it dry in the oven at 110°C for *at least* 30 minutes. When it is dry and *cool,* find its mass on the analytical balance. If you have time, dry it an additional 30 minutes and again determine its mass to see if it reached a constant value.

7. Calculate the Percent Silver in the Alloy.

From your data, determine the percent of silver in your sample.

Disposal

The solid silver chloride and the filter pad may be disposed of according to Flinn Suggested Disposal Method #26a. The solution from which the silver was precipitated can be disposed of according to Flinn Suggested Disposal Method #24b. Consult your instructor, the *Flinn Chemical & Biological Catalog/Reference Manual,* or see the appendix of the teacher's manual.

If a sintered glass crucible is used, the AgCl can be cleaned from it by soaking it in a 6 M ammonia, NH_3, solution.

Discussion

In your laboratory report include answers to the following:

1. Show how your calculations are carried out.

2. Why is a twofold excess of chloride added to precipitate the silver?

3. Why don't you have to weigh the sodium chloride on a sensitive balance?

4. Why is it necessary to wash the precipitate?

5. Will the nitric acid in the wash water interfere with the weight of the silver chloride? (Nitric acid is prepared by dissolving the gas N_2O_5 in water.)

6. If the crucible containing the silver chloride is not cool when its mass is determined, will the calculated percent silver be too high or too low? Why?

7. Why don't we just use hydrochloric acid to both dissolve and precipitate the silver?

8. Why is a special filter crucible, rather than plain filter paper used?

Analysis of Silver in an Alloy

Preliminary Lab Assignment

Name_____ Date_____ Class_____

1. What is the difference between qualitative and quantitative analytical methods?

2. Why is it possible to analyze the silver content of a silver–copper alloy by precipitating with chloride ion?

3. Is there any other ion besides chloride that could be used in this procedure? If so, why would this ion work?

4. A silver–copper alloy had a mass of 0.1264 g. When the alloy was dissolved and the silver precipitated as silver chloride, the precipitate had a mass of 0.1375 g. Calculate the percent of silver in the alloy. Show your calculations.

5. If the silver chloride is not dry when its mass is determined, will the calculated percent of silver in the alloy be too high or too low? Explain.

FLINN SCIENTIFIC

Finding the Ratio of Moles of Reactants in a Chemical Reaction

A balanced chemical equation gives the mole ratios of reactants and products for chemical reactions. If the formulas of all reactants and products are known, it is relatively easy to balance an equation to find out what these mole ratios are. When the formulas of the products are not known, experimental measurements must be made to determine the ratios.

This experiment uses the *method of continuous variations* to determine the mole ratio of two reactants. Several steps are involved. First, solutions of the reactants are prepared in which the concentrations are known. Second, the solutions are mixed a number of times using different ratios of reactants. Third, some property of the reaction that depends on the amount of product formed or on the amount of reactant that remains is measured. This property may be the color intensity of a reactant or product, the mass of a precipitate that forms, or the volume of a gas evolved. In this experiment the change of temperature is the property to be measured. The reactions are all exothermic, so the heat produced will be directly proportional to the amount of reaction that occurs. Since the experiment is designed so that the volume of solution is constant for all measurements, the temperature change will also be proportional to the extent that the reaction occurs.

In the method of continuous variations, the total number of moles of reactants is kept constant for the series of measurements. Each measurement is made with a different mole ratio of reactants. The optimum ratio, which is the stoichiometric ratio in the equation, should consume the greatest amount of reactants, form the greatest amount of product, and generate the most heat and maximum temperature change.

Chemicals

Sodium hypochlorite, $NaClO$, 0.50 M

Sodium thiosulfate, $Na_2S_2O_3$, 0.50 M in NaOH, 0.20 M

   or Potassium iodide, KI, 0.50 M in NaOH, 0.20 M

   or Sodium sulfite, Na_2SO_3, 0.50 M in NaOH, 0.20 M

   as "Solution B"

Equipment

Styrofoam® cup	Graduated cylinder, 10-mL
Thermometer	Graduated cylinder, 25- or 50-mL

Procedure

Safety Alert

NaClO is a bleach. Keep it off of clothing. All solutions are basic and harmful to skin and eyes. If you spill any, wash off with copious amounts of water. Work in a hood or under a funnel attached to an aspirator since fumes may be given off.

Wear Chemical Splash Goggles and a Chemical-Resistant Apron.

1. **Find the Starting Temperature.**

   Measure the temperature of the NaClO solution and of "Solution B", the second solution that you have chosen. Record your data in a table. Use the same thermometer or a pair of calibrated thermometers. The solutions should be the same temperature. If they are not, you will need to make a correction for the temperature difference.

2. **Mix Solutions and Measure Temperature Changes.**

   Pour 5.0 mL of NaClO into a styrofoam cup, and then add 45.0 mL of the second solution. Stir with a thermometer, and record the highest temperature reached by the mixture. Pour the solution out, rinse the cup and thermometer, and repeat the process using a different ratio of the two substances, always keeping the total volume at 50.0 mL. Continue testing various ratios until you have *at least three measurements on each side of the one that gave the maximum temperature*.

3. **Plot the Data.**

   Plot your data as shown in Figure 1. Draw two straight lines that best fit your data, and determine where they intersect. Be sure to include the points at the 0:50 mL and 50:0 mL ratios. If any points do not fall close to the lines, you should repeat these measurements. Find the stoichiometric mole ratio of reactants from the point of intersection on your graph.

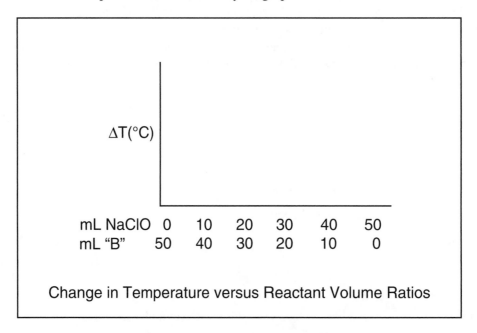

Figure 1. Graph of Experimental Data

Technology

The data may be plotted using a spreadsheet program or a graphing program such as *Graphical Analysis for Windows*.

Disposal

The solutions may be flushed down the drain with excess water.

Discussion

In your laboratory report include answers to the following:

1. Explain how this method allows you to find the mole ratio of reactants.

2. Why must you keep a constant volume of reactants?

3. Is it necessary that the concentrations of the two solutions be the same?

4. What is meant by the term limiting reagent?

5. Which measurement, temperature or volume, limits the precision of your data? Explain.

6. Which reactant is the limiting reagent along the upward sloping line of your graph? Which is the limiting reagent along the downward sloping line?

7. What physical properties, other than temperature change, could use the method of continuous variations?

8. Why is it more accurate to use the point of intersection of the two lines to find the mole ratio rather than the ratio associated with the greatest temperature change?

9. If the two solutions used are not at the same initial temperature, a correction must be made to find the correct change in temperature. How should this be done?

References

Additional information on the continuous variations method may be found in the following:

Alexander, J. J.; Steffel, M. J. *Chemistry in the Laboratory*; Burgess International Group: Edina, MN, 1988; p 47.

Mahoney, D. W.; Sweeney, J. A.; Davenport, D. A.; Ramette, R. W.; *J. Chem. Educ.* **1981**, *58*, 730.

Finding the Ratio of Moles of Reactants in a Chemical Reaction

Preliminary Lab Assignment

Name_____ Date_____ Class_____

1. The following values were obtained in a continuous variations experiment designed to find the coefficients in the equation for the reaction between 0.5 M solutions of $AgNO_3$ and K_2CrO_4. One of the products is a precipitate:

Experiment	mL $AgNO_3$	mL K_2CrO_4	Grams Precipitate
1	5.0	45.0	1.7
2	15.0	35.0	5.0
3	25.0	25.0	8.3
4	30.0	20.0	10.0
5	35.0	15.0	9.9
6	40.0	10.0	6.6
7	45.0	5.0	3.3

Plot the data as shown in the lab directions. Label axes and space the data so that the graph reflects the precision of the values given. Use a ruler to draw the best-fitting straight lines, and determine the stoichiometry of the reaction.

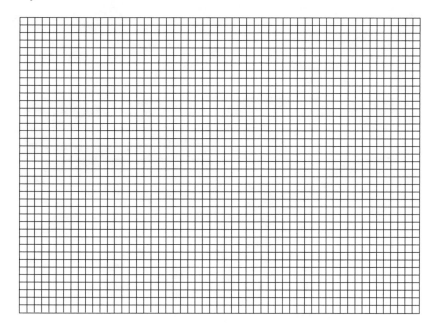

_____ $AgNO_3$ + _____ K_2CrO_4 → Products

2. Are there enough values to make a valid conclusion? Why or why not?

Synthesis of Alum, $KAl(SO_4)_2 \cdot 12H_2O$

In this experiment the ionic compound, potassium aluminum sulfate ($KAl(SO_4)_2 \cdot 12H_2O$), is prepared from a water solution that contains K^+, Al^{3+} and SO_4^{2-} (potassium, aluminum, and sulfate ions, respectively). The aluminum ions will be formed by oxidizing aluminum from aluminum foil. The "double salt" potassium aluminum sulfate dodecahydrate is commonly referred to as alum. Many combinations of mono- and tri-positive cations yield crystals of the same stoichiometry and structure, and alum is a general name for this type of compound. For example, there is chrome alum, $KCr(SO_4)_2 \cdot 12H_2O$, which is a deep purple color, as well as alums where either sodium or ammonium ions are present instead of the potassium ion. The crystals are usually in the shape of octahedra.

If an aqueous solution which contains $[Al(H_2O)_6]^{3+}$ ions, K^+ ions and SO_4^{2-} ions is evaporated, the compound $KAl(SO_4)_2 \cdot 12H_2O$ crystallizes. Within the alum crystal, six waters of hydration are bonded directly to the aluminum ion to give $[Al(H_2O)_6]^{3+}$ ions, while the other six surround the K^+ ion.

Alum crystals of great purity are easily prepared. Because of this purity, alum is useful in the dyeing of cloth, where the alum acts as a source of Al^{3+} ions which are not contaminated with Fe^{3+}. The Al^{3+} is precipitated on the cloth as aluminum hydroxide which acts as a binding agent for dyes. It is necessary that no Fe^{3+} be present in order to produce clear colors.

Aluminum is considered a reactive metal, but because its surface is usually protected by a thin film of aluminum oxide, it reacts only slowly with acids. It does, however, dissolve quickly in basic solutions. Excess hydroxide ion converts the aluminum to the tetrahydroxoaluminate(III) ion, $[Al(OH)_4]^-$. When acid is slowly added to this ion, white, gelatinous aluminum hydroxide ($Al(OH)_3$) precipitates. Continued addition of acid causes the hydroxide ions to be completely neutralized, and the aluminum exists in solution as the hydrated ion $[Al(H_2O)_6]^{3+}$. Aluminum hydroxide is called an "amphoteric" hydroxide because it dissolves in both acids and bases.

Chemicals

Aluminum foil

Sulfuric acid, H_2SO_4, 3 M

Baking soda, $NaHCO_3(s)$

pH paper or litmus paper

Potassium hydroxide, KOH, 3 M

Water–ethanol (or isopropanol) solution, 50% by volume

Vinegar, dilute $HC_2H_3O_2$

Equipment

Beaker, 250-mL

Graduated cylinder

Büchner funnel and filter flask

Ice bath

Balance

Watch glass

Stirring rod

Burner, ring stand, ring, wire gauze (or hot plate)

Plastic wrap or Parafilm®

Fume hood

Safety Alert

You will be using solutions with high concentrations of sulfuric acid and potassium hydroxide, both of which are highly damaging to skin and eyes. Be careful when handling them. If you spill any on yourself, wash off with lots of water. Neutralize sulfuric acid spills on the counter with baking soda, and neutralize potassium hydroxide spills with vinegar (dilute acetic acid).

When aluminum dissolves in potassium hydroxide solution, hydrogen gas is produced. Make sure that no flames are present. This step should be performed in a fume hood.

Boiling concentrated solutions often results in bumping and spurting of the hot liquid. **Protect yourself with a safety shield, or heat inside a hood behind the window.**

Add several boiling stones to the solution (remove with a forceps before you find the mass of the crystals). Alternatively, make a boiling tube by taking a piece of glass tubing about 20 cm long, and sealing one end by heating and pinching the molten glass closed with a forceps. Leave the other end open and not fire-polished. Use the boiling tube by leaving it in the boiling solution, open end down, acting as a sit for the liquid-vapor phase change.

Wear Chemical Splash Goggles and a Chemical-Resistant Apron.

Procedure

1. **Weigh Out and Dissolve the Aluminum.**

   Weigh out about 1 gram of aluminum foil to the nearest centigram. Tear the foil into small pieces and place in a 250 mL beaker.

   Slowly add 25 mL of 3 M KOH solution. Allow the reaction to proceed until all of the foil is dissolved. Remove any undissolved solids such as carbon particles by filtering the solution through a Büchner funnel while the solution is hot. Rinse the filter paper with a small amount of distilled water.

2. **Acidify with Sulfuric Acid.**

   At this point the solution contains $[Al(OH)_4]^-$ and K^+ ions, along with excess OH^- ions. Cool the solution and then acidify it SLOWLY, with constant stirring, using 35 mL of 3 M H_2SO_4. The solution will get

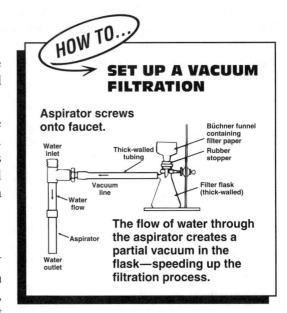

HOW TO...

SET UP A VACUUM FILTRATION

Aspirator screws onto faucet.

Water inlet

Thick-walled tubing

Büchner funnel containing filter paper

Rubber stopper

Vacuum line

Filter flask (thick-walled)

Water flow

Aspirator

Water outlet

The flow of water through the aspirator creates a partial vacuum in the flask—speeding up the filtration process.

very hot because you are adding strong acid to the strongly basic solution. Solid $Al(OH)_3$ will first precipitate and then dissolve as more H_2SO_4 is added. If a precipitate still remains, check with litmus or pH paper to be sure the solution is acidic. If not, add 5 mL more H_2SO_4, filter the solution and discard the solids. You can use vacuum filtration with a Büchner funnel and filter flask to speed up this process. (Refer to the Safety Alert above.) Then boil the solution until water has evaporated to give a volume of about 50 mL of solution. This is a good place to stop if the end of the lab period is near. Cool the solution and cover the beaker with Parafilm® or plastic wrap. Allow it to rest undisturbed until the next period.

3. Crystallize the Alum.

If time permits, cool the solution in an ice bath for 15 minutes, keeping it as motionless as possible, or let it stand overnight. Crystals of alum should grow in the beaker. If no crystals form, scrape the bottom of the beaker with a stirring rod to create a rough place where crystals may begin to grow, or add a seed crystal. If there are still no crystals, reheat the solution until more water has evaporated and then cool again. Rapid cooling in an ice bath causes very small crystals to grow; slow overnight cooling allows the formation of larger crystals. Collect the alum crystals by vacuum filtration. Wash the crystals with 50 mL of a 50% by volume water and ethanol (or isopropanol) mixture, in which alum crystals are not very soluble. Allow the crystals to dry at room temperature. Determine the mass of the alum. Calculate the theoretical yield of alum assuming that aluminum was the limiting reactant and that the foil was 100% aluminum, and calculate your percent yield.

Verify that your crystals are alum by performing Experiment 4, "Analysis of Alum."

Disposal

Pour the filtrate into a beaker which your instructor will provide for disposal. See the *Flinn Chemical & Biological Catalog/Reference Manual*, Flinn Suggested Disposal Method #24b, or see the appendix of the teacher's manual.

Discussion

Answer the following questions in your laboratory report:

1. Write balanced net ionic equations for the following reactions which occur in this synthesis:

   a) Aluminum reacts with KOH and water forming potassium ions, $[Al(OH)_4]^-$ and hydrogen gas.

   b) Hydrogen ions from the acid react with the tetrahydroxoaluminate ions to precipitate aluminum hydroxide.

   c) Aluminum hydroxide reacts with additional hydrogen ions and water to form $[Al(H_2O)_6]^{3+}$

   d) Alum forms from the potassium ions, hydrated aluminum ions, sulfate ions and water.

2. What is a "synthesis" reaction?

3. Why should you NOT expect a 100% yield of crystals?

4. How does the solubility of alum in water change with temperature?

5. Why should you NOT wash the crystals with pure water?

6. What do your crystals look like?

7. What is the shape of an octahedron?

8. Show how you obtained your theoretical and percent yields.

Synthesis of Alum, KAl(SO$_4$)$_2$·12H$_2$O

Preliminary Lab Assignment

Name_____ Date_____ Class_____

1. What is alum?

2. What is a hydrated crystal?

3. What is meant by the term amphoteric?

4. Write a balanced net ionic equation showing aluminum hydroxide dissolving in a solution containing excess hydroxide ion.

5. Write a balanced net ionic equation showing aluminum hydroxide dissolving in an acid solution.

6. If a reaction to synthesize KAl(SO$_4$)$_2$·12H$_2$O is carried out using 1.0 g of potassium metal as the limiting reagent, what is the maximum mass of alum that can form? Show your calculations.

7. If the procedure in question 6 is carried out and 4.5 g of alum is actually obtained, what would be the percent yield? Show your calculations.

FLINN SCIENTIFIC

LABORATORY NOTES

Analysis of Alum, $KAl(SO_4)_2 \cdot 12H_2O$

After a compound has been synthesized, tests should be carried out to verify that the compound formed is indeed the compound desired. There are a number of various tests that can be performed to verify that the compound is the one desired. In the previous experiment, alum crystals, $KAl(SO_4)_2 \cdot 12H_2O$, were prepared. In this experiment we carry out several tests to determine if the crystals are really alum. Alternatively, you may be given an unknown compound to analyze.

The first and simplest test is to find the melting point of the compound and compare it to the published value for alum. A small quantity of alum is powdered and placed in a capillary tube which is attached by a rubber band to a thermometer bulb. The crystals are heated in a water bath, and the temperature at which they melt is recorded and compared to reported values.

The second test that we can do is to determine the amount of water of hydration present in the alum crystals. Some of the alum is placed in a crucible and weighed. The crucible is heated until all of the water of hydration is driven off. The crucible is then cooled and its mass measured. From the mass of the dry crystals and the mass of the water lost, the ratio of moles water to moles $KAl(SO_4)_2$ can be calculated and then compared to the correct formula values.

The third test is a chemical test to determine the percent of sulfate in the compound prepared. A weighed quantity of alum is dissolved in distilled water. An excess of barium ions is added to the solution to precipitate all of the sulfate in the compound as barium sulfate. The precipitated barium sulfate is filtered off, dried, and its mass determined. From the mass of the barium sulfate and the initial mass of alum, the percent sulfate can be calculated and compared with the theoretical percent found from the formula.

Chemicals

Parts 1, 2 and 3

Alum crystals, $KAl(SO_4)_2 \cdot 12H_2O$ (or an unknown compound)

Part 3

Barium nitrate, $Ba(NO_3)_2$, 0.2 M

Equipment

Part 1

Capillary tube	Thermometer
Beaker (or Thiele melting point tube)	Rubber band
Ring stand, ring, wire gauze	Universal clamp
Cork (or split stopper) to hold thermometer	Stirring rod
Mortar and pestle (or test tube and watch glass)	Bunsen burner (or hot plate)

Part 2

Crucible and cover	Ring stand, ring, Bunsen burner (or oven)
Triangle	Triangle support

Part 3

Beaker, 250-mL	Graduated cylinder, 25-mL
Stirring rod	Ring stand, ring, Bunsen burner (or hot plate)
Rubber policeman	Wash bottle with distilled water
Watch glass	Aspirator
Gooch crucible with fiber glass filter pad, filter flask and adapter (or funnel and fine grained filter paper)	

Procedure

Safety Alert

Be cautious using flames.

Barium nitrate is very poisonous. Wash your hands when finished with the experiment.

Wear Chemical Splash Goggles and a Chemical-Resistant Apron.

Part 1. Find the Melting Point of Alum.

Pulverize a small amount (about 0.5 g) of dry alum. Use a mortar and pestle, or use a watch glass and the bottom of a test tube. Pack the alum in a capillary tube to a depth of about 1 cm. To get the alum into the capillary tube, push the open end of the capillary down into a small pile of alum powder. Then turn the tube so the open end is up, and bounce the bottom of the tube on the desk top. You may also pack the alum by holding a long piece of 6 mm diameter glass tubing (1 m in length) upright on the floor, and dropping the capillary tube down the glass tubing. The capillary tube will bounce up and down a few times which will pack the powder.

Cut a 1 mm length of rubber tubing to use as a rubber band, and with it fasten the capillary tube to a thermometer. The alum should be level with the bulb of the thermometer. Use a universal clamp and cork stopper (or split rubber stopper) to fasten the thermometer to a ring stand. Immerse the bottom of the capillary and thermometer in a beaker of water (or a Thiele melting point tube filled with water) and heat. If using a beaker, you must stir the water to maintain an even distribution of temperature. You may heat rapidly in the beginning but as you get close to the melting point, heat very slowly in order to get an accurate value. Record the temperature at which the alum melts (the white powder will become clear). If you wish to repeat the melting procedure, use both a new sample and a new capillary tube.

Find the published value for the melting point of alum, and compare the experimental and published values.

Part 2. Determine the Amount of Water of Hydration in Alum Crystals.

Heat a crucible with a cover over a burner flame until it is red hot. Allow them to cool, and find their mass using a sensitive balance. Handle with tongs or forceps to avoid getting fingerprints on them. Now add about 2 g of alum crystals to the crucible. Accurately determine the mass of the crucible, cover, and crystals.

Set the crucible at an angle in a triangle held in a ring on a ring stand, cover loosely with the crucible cover, and heat very gently. The alum crystals will melt, and the water of hydration will vaporize. It is important that the escaping vapor does not carry any of the anhydrous alum along with it, so be sure that the crystals are heated very gently at first. After the vapor is apparently driven off, heat more strongly for five minutes. Cool, and find the mass of the crucible, cover, and anhydrous alum.

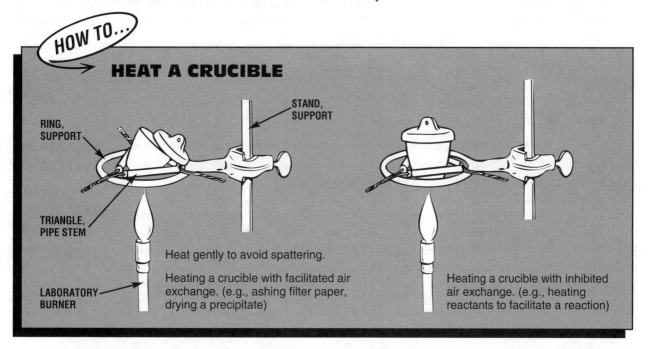

HOW TO...

HEAT A CRUCIBLE

STAND, SUPPORT

RING, SUPPORT

TRIANGLE, PIPE STEM

LABORATORY BURNER

Heat gently to avoid spattering.

Heating a crucible with facilitated air exchange. (e.g., ashing filter paper, drying a precipitate)

Heating a crucible with inhibited air exchange. (e.g., heating reactants to facilitate a reaction)

Alternatively, the water of hydration can also be driven off by heating the crucible containing alum in an oven at 110°C overnight.

Calculate the mass of the anhydrous alum and the mass of the water that was driven off. Find the moles of anhydrous $KAl(SO_4)_2$, and the moles of H_2O. Calculate the ratio of moles H_2O:moles $KAl(SO_4)_2$, and give the calculated formula of alum, $KAl(SO_4)_2 \cdot XH_2O$, where X = the ratio of moles H_2O:moles $KAl(SO_4)_2$. Compare your value with that of alum.

Repeat the drying procedure until constant mass is obtained.

Part 3. Determine the Percent Sulfate in Alum.

Obtain a Gooch crucible with fiber glass filter pad, Walters adapter and filter flask. See Figure 1 in "Analysis of Silver in an Alloy" for a diagram to show the proper assembly. Use suction to pull distilled water through the filter pad, place the crucible in a beaker and dry it in a drying oven. After it is cool, determine its mass using a sensitive balance. Barium sulfate crystallizes as very tiny particles, so a filter crucible works well. If no Gooch crucible is available, use a funnel and fine-grained filter paper (for example, Whatman No. 42 or Schliecher and Schuell No. 589, blue or red ribbon). Measure the mass of a piece of the filter paper.

Use the sensitive balance to accurately weigh about 1 gram of alum into a 250 mL beaker. Dissolve in approximately 50 mL of distilled water. Calculate the volume of 0.2 M $Ba(NO_3)_2$ which would be needed to totally precipitate all of the sulfate ion present in solution, and then add twice this volume of $Ba(NO_3)_2$ slowly, while stirring.

Cover the beaker with a watch glass and heat the solution nearly to boiling. Keep the solution just under the boiling point for at least 15 minutes. During this time, the precipitate particles grow to a filterable size. Alternatively, cover the beaker and allow the precipitate to stand overnight.

Filter the precipitate through the filter crucible with suction. Do not fill the crucible too full as the barium sulfate has a tendency to "creep" up the sides. Use a rubber policeman to be sure that every particle is transferred from the beaker and stirring rod into the filter crucible. (Alternatively, filter the precipitate through the fine filter paper.) Wash the beaker and then the precipitate several times with small quantities of distilled water.

Carefully transfer the filter crucible to a beaker and dry it in an oven. (Air dry the filter paper or dry it in an oven at 50°C so that it does not char.) Allow the dry filter crucible (or paper) to cool and determine its mass.

Calculate the percent sulfate present in the alum and compare to the value calculated from its formula.

Disposal

Parts 1 and 2

Your teacher will provide marked containers in which you should place your used capillary tubes and the anhydrous alum. Consult the *Flinn Chemical & Biological Catalog/Reference Manual*, Flinn Suggested Disposal Method #26a, or see the appendix of the teacher's manual.

Part 3

Your teacher will provide containers in which you can place the precipitated barium sulfate and the filtrate you collected. The filtrate will contain excess barium nitrate as well as potassium and aluminum ions. Consult the current *Flinn Chemical & Biological Catalog/Reference Manual,* Suggested Disposal Method #27h for disposal of barium compounds. For disposal of the residual solution, please consult the *Flinn Chemical & Biological Catalog/Reference Manual*, Flinn Suggested Disposal Method #26b, or see the appendix of the teacher's manual.

Discussion

In your laboratory report, include all calculations and measurements and answer the following questions:

1. Why must objects be cooled before their mass is found on a sensitive balance?

2. Comment on the results of the different tests you used to verify that the substance tested was alum.

3. What other tests could be made to verify the composition of alum?

Analysis of Alum, $KAl(SO_4)_2 \cdot 12H_2O$

Preliminary Lab Assignment

Name_____ Date_____ Class_____

1. When finding a melting point, why is it necessary to raise the temperature very slowly when approaching the melting temperature?

2. Washing soda is a hydrated compound whose formula can be written $Na_2CO_3 \cdot XH_2O$, where X is the number of moles of H_2O per mole of Na_2CO_3. When a 2.123 g sample of washing soda is heated at 130°C, all of the water of hydration is lost leaving 0.789 g of anhydrous sodium carbonate. Calculate the value of X.

3. The formula for epsom salts is $MgSO_4 \cdot 7H_2O$. If 1.250 g of the compound is dissolved in water, calculate the number of milliliters of 0.200 M $Ba(NO_3)_2$ which would be required to just precipitate all of the sulfate as barium sulfate.

FLINN SCIENTIFIC

LABORATORY NOTES

An Activity Series

In this experiment, some metals and some nonmetals are studied to find their relative reactivity. A ranking according to reactivity is called an activity series. For example, an activity series containing the elements calcium, gold and iron would put the reactive calcium at the top, iron in the middle, and the unreactive gold at the bottom. If a piece of iron metal is placed in a solution of gold nitrate, the iron will dissolve forming positive ions while the solid gold metal appears. The more reactive metal will displace ions of the less reactive metal from solution. The less reactive element appears as the solid element.

Reactions such as these are all oxidation–reduction reactions. Oxidation is defined as loss of electrons. Substances which lose electrons during chemical reactions are said to be oxidized. Those which gain electrons are reduced. If one reactant gains electrons, another must lose an equal number of electrons. Oxidation and reduction reactions must occur simultaneously, and there must be an equal number of electrons lost and gained. In the above example, the iron metal would be oxidized and the gold ions would be reduced. The most reactive metal is the one most easily oxidized.

When a substance readily loses electrons (and is oxidized), it acts as a good reducing agent. When a substance has a strong tendency to gain electrons (and be reduced), it also acts as a good oxidizing agent. Gold ions, Au^{3+}, have a strong tendency to acquire electrons to form neutral gold atoms, Au. Gold ions are easily reduced and act as good oxidizing agents.

An activity series of the nonmetallic halogens places the most reactive halogen at the top. Like the metals, the more reactive nonmetals will displace ions of the less reactive halides from solution. In an activity series of nonmetals, the most reactive halogen is the one most easily reduced.

The first part of this experiment derives an activity series for metals and uses a microscale technique. The second part derives an activity series for halogens. It makes use of a solvent extraction technique.

Chemicals

Part 1

Copper, Cu(s)   Copper(II) nitrate, 0.1 M, $Cu(NO_3)_2$

Zinc, Zn(s)   Zinc nitrate, 0.1 M, $Zn(NO_3)_2$

Magnesium, Mg(s)   Magnesium nitrate, 0.1 M, $Mg(NO_3)_2$

Lead, Pb(s)   Lead(II) nitrate, 0.1 M, $Pb(NO_3)_2$

Silver nitrate, 0.1 M, $AgNO_3$

Part 2

Chlorine water, Cl_2(aq)   Sodium chloride, 0.1 M, NaCl

Bromine water, Br_2(aq)   Sodium bromide, 0.1 M, NaBr

Iodine water, I_2(aq)   Potassium iodide, 0.1 M, KI

Mineral oil

Equipment

Part 1

24-well plate   Forceps
Stirring rod

Part 2

Test tubes, 13- × 100-mm   Cork stoppers for test tubes
Test tube rack

Procedure

Safety Alert

Silver nitrate stains skin and clothing. The stains do not appear for several hours. If you spill any on yourself, wash off with soap and water immediately.

Lead compounds are very poisonous. Wash your hands thoroughly when finished.

Wear Chemical Splash Goggles and a Chemical-Resistant Apron.

Part 1. Determine an Activity Series for Some Metals.

Place the 24-well plate so that there are 6 wells across (rows) and 4 wells down (columns). Refer to Figure 1 to see how the chemical solutions are arranged.

Place one dropper full (about 15 drops or 1 mL) of copper(II) nitrate solution in wells 2 through 4 in the first column. Put one dropper full of magnesium nitrate in wells 1, 3, and 4 of the second column. Place one dropper full of lead(II) nitrate in wells 1, 2, and 4 of the third column. Put one dropper full of zinc nitrate in wells 1, 2, and 3 of the fourth column, and put one dropper full of silver nitrate in each of the 4 wells in the fifth column.

Put a small piece of copper metal in each of the wells containing a solution in the first row. Add magnesium metal to the solutions in the second row, lead to the third row, and zinc to the fourth row. Use a stirring rod to submerge the metal pieces. Allow to stand at least 5 minutes. Determine if a reaction has occurred in each well by observing if a metal precipitate has formed or if the surface of the metal has become coated. If a metal ion is reduced by a metal, than the reverse reaction should not occur. One metal is more reactive than another if the metal will replace the metal ion (reduce it) in its compounds. (You can begin the next part while you are waiting.) Record your data.

	Cu^{2+}(aq)	Mg^{2+}(aq)	Pb^{2+}(aq)	Zn^{2+}(aq)	Ag^{+}(aq)	
Cu(s)	×					×
Mg(s)		×				×
Pb(s)			×			×
Zn(s)				×		×

Figure 1. Arrangement of Solutions and Metals in 24-Well Plate

Wells marked with × are empty.

Disposal

Your instructor will provide a container in which you can discard the solutions. Some crumpled aluminum foil will be placed in the solution and it will be allowed to stand for a day. The metals silver, copper and lead will all plate out of solution leaving essentially none of these ions dissolved. The metals can then be filtered out and disposed of in an approved landfill. Consult the current *Flinn Chemical & Biological Catalog/Reference Manual,* Flinn Suggested Disposal Methods #26a and #26b, or see the appendix of the teacher's manual.

Clean the 24-well plate with detergent and water using cotton swabs if needed.

Part 2. Determine an Activity Series for Some Halogens.

Safety Alert

Chlorine, bromine and iodine water solutions have strong odors. Avoid breathing them.

In this part you will test to see if the halogens Cl_2, Br_2, and I_2 can be reduced by the halide ions Cl^-, Br^-, and I^-. To determine what products will be formed, you will need to have a test which will tell which halogen is present. Halogens dissolve in the nonpolar solvent mineral oil forming different colored solutions. Mineral oil does not dissolve in water, but when shaken with an aqueous halogen solution, the halogen is extracted from the water into the mineral oil. The color of the mineral oil layer indicates which halogen is present.

First, test to see what color each halogen is when dissolved in mineral oil. Place one dropper of chlorine water, one dropper of bromine water, and one dropper of iodine water into separate 10 mm test tubes. Add one dropper of mineral oil to each, cork the tube and shake it for ten seconds. Let the mineral oil layer rise to the top and record the color that each halogen shows when dissolved in mineral oil.

Test to see if the halide ions give a color to mineral oil. Place one dropper of NaCl, KI, and NaBr solutions into different test tubes, add a dropper of mineral oil to each, cork and shake to determine if the halide ions impart a color to the mineral oil layer. Report your data.

React each halogen with the other two halide ions to see if a halide ion can reduce other halogens. Place one dropper of NaBr solution into one test tube and one dropper of KI solution into a second test tube. Add one dropper chlorine water to each, cork and shake to mix. Now add one dropper of mineral oil, cork and shake again. When the mineral oil layer has separated, record its color and determine if a reaction has occurred. Use a table similar to that shown in Figure 2 to record your data. If the color of the chlorine appears in the mineral oil layer then no reaction has occurred. If either bromine or iodine appears, then there was a reaction.

Repeat the test using bromine water mixed with NaCl and KI solutions, and iodine water mixed with NaCl and NaBr solutions.

	$Cl_2(aq)$	$Br_2(aq)$	$I_2(aq)$
$Cl^-(aq)$	×		
$Br^-(aq)$		×	
$I^-(aq)$			×

Figure 2. Combinations of Halogens and Halide Ions

Combinations marked with × are not necessary.

Disposal

Empty the test tubes in the container provided for disposal. Use a different container than the one used in Part 1. Your instructor will place this container in the hood for several days during which the halogens will evaporate from the solution. The remaining solution can then be flushed down the drain with a 20-fold excess of water. Consult the *Flinn Chemical & Biological Catalog/Reference Manual*, Flinn Suggested Disposal Method #26b, or see the appendix of the teacher's manual.

Discussion

In your laboratory report, include all your data and answer the following questions:

1. Write balanced net ionic equations for all the reactions that occurred with the metals.

2. List the metals in order of decreasing ease of oxidation. Compare your list with an activity series found in a textbook. How do the two lists correlate?

3. Write reduction half-reactions for each of the metal ions. Arrange the reaction list in order of decreasing ease of reduction. Compare your listing with a listing found in a table of standard reduction potentials. How do the two lists correlate?

4. Explain what is meant by solvent extraction.

5. Explain how you can tell if a reaction occurs in the halogen experiment.

6. Why should you not expect the halide ions to dissolve in mineral oil?

7. Write balanced net ionic equations for the reactions which occurred with the halogens.

8. List the halogens in decreasing order of reactivity. Compare your list with an activity series found in a textbook. How do the two lists correlate?

9. Write reduction half-reactions for each of the halogens. Arrange in order of decreasing ease of reduction. Compare the listing with the order found in a table of standard reduction potentials. How do the lists correlate?

10. Why is it necessary to test the halide ions for color?

An Activity Series

Preliminary Lab Assignment

Name_____ Date_____ Class_____

1. Define oxidation.

2. Define reduction.

3. Explain the fact that a good oxidizing agent is easily reduced.

4. An activity series for metals contains the following listing:

    Most reactive: Aluminum

                                Iron

                                Nickel

    Least reactive: Platinum

    Predict if the following reactions will occur. Explain your answer.

    a) $2 \, Al^{3+}(aq) + 3 \, Pt(s) \rightarrow 2 \, Al(s) + 3 \, Pt^{2+}(aq)$

    b) $Fe(s) + Ni^{2+}(aq) \rightarrow Fe^{2+}(aq) + Ni(s)$

    c) $Pt^{2+}(aq) + Fe(s) \rightarrow Pt(s) + Fe^{2+}(aq)$

FLINN SCIENTIFIC

LABORATORY NOTES

Thermochemistry and Hess's Law

In this experiment the enthalpy change that occurs when sodium hydroxide and hydrochloric acid solutions are mixed is determined. Next, the enthalpy change for the reaction between sodium hydroxide and ammonium chloride is measured. Lastly, the enthalpy change for the reaction between ammonia and hydrochloric acid is found. An algebraic combination of the first two equations can lead to the third equation. Therefore, according to Hess's law, an algebraic combination of the enthalpy changes of the first two should lead to the enthalpy of the third reaction.

The molecular equations for the reactions are as follows:

(1) $NaOH(aq) + HCl(aq) \rightarrow NaCl(aq) + H_2O(l)$

(2) $NH_4Cl(aq) + NaOH(aq) \rightarrow NH_3(aq) + NaCl(aq) + H_2O(l)$

(3) $NH_3(aq) + HCl(aq) \rightarrow NH_4Cl(aq)$

According to Hess, if a reaction can be carried out in a series of steps, the sum of the enthalpies for each step should equal the enthalpy change for the total reaction. Another way of stating "Hess's Law" is: If two chemical equations can algebraically be combined to give a third equation, the values of ΔH for the two equations can be combined in the same manner to give ΔH for the third equation. An examination of the acid–base equations above shows that if equation (2) is subtracted from equation (1), equation (3) will result. Therefore, if the value of ΔH for equation (2) is subtracted from that of equation (1), the enthalpy change for equation (3) should result. We will test this idea in this experiment.

There is no single instrument that can directly measure heat in the way a balance measures mass or a thermometer measures temperature. However, it is possible to calculate gain or loss of heat when a chemical reaction occurs. The change in heat is calculated from the mass, temperature change, and specific heat of the substance which gains or loses heat.

The equation that is used to calculate heat gain or loss is:

$$q = (\text{grams of substance}) \times (\text{specific heat}) \times \Delta T$$

where q = the heat energy gained or lost and ΔT is the change in temperature. Since ΔT = (final temperature minus initial temperature), an increase in temperature will result in a positive value for both ΔT and q, and a loss of heat will give a negative value. A positive value for q means a heat gain, while a negative value means a heat loss.

Acid–base neutralization is an exothermic process. Combining solutions containing an acid and a base results in a rise of solution temperature. The heat given off by the reaction (which causes the solution temperature to rise) can be calculated from the specific heat of the solution, the mass of solution and the temperature change. This heat quantity can then be converted to the enthalpy change for the reaction in terms of kJ/mole by using the concentrations of the reactants.

Chemicals

Hydrochloric acid, HCl, 2.0 M

Sodium hydroxide, NaOH, 2.0 M

Ammonia, NH_3, 2.0 M

Ammonium chloride, NH_4Cl, 2.0 M

Baking soda, $NaHCO_3$(s),

Vinegar, $HC_2H_3O_2$(aq)

Equipment

Graduated cylinder, 25- or 50-mL

Beaker

Calorimeter made of two nested Styrofoam® Cups
and a cover

Fume hood

Magnetic stirrer and stirring bar (optional)

Ring stand, ring, wire gauze, Bunsen burner
(or hot plate)

Thermometer (preferably one that is
calibrated ± 0.1°C)

Procedure

Safety Alert

You will be working with strong acids and bases in concentrated solutions. The ammonia and hydrochloric acid have strong odors. If you spill any on yourself, wash off with lots of water. Neutralize acid spills on the lab bench with baking soda. Neutralize ammonia and sodium hydroxide spills with vinegar, which is dilute acetic acid.

Wear Chemical Splash Goggles and a Chemical-Resistant Apron.

1. Find the Heat Capacity of the Calorimeter.

Construct a calorimeter of two nested Styrofoam cups with a cover which has a hole in it to accept a thermometer. Measure 50.0 mL of distilled water at room temperature into the calorimeter. Place the assembly on a magnetic stirring motor, add a magnet and turn on the motor so the stirring bar spins slowly. (Alternatively, gently stir the solution with your thermometer.) Now record the temperature as precisely as you can.

Heat about 75 mL of distilled water to about 70°C. Measure 50.0 mL of this water into a different Styrofoam cup and precisely record its temperature. Immediately pour the hot water into the room temperature water, cover, insert the thermometer, stir and record the temperature every 20 seconds for three minutes.

2. Find the Heat of the Reactions.

Determine the temperature change that occurs when 50.0 mL of 2.0 M HCl solution reacts with 50.0 mL of 2.0 M NaOH. First, measure the temperature of each of the solutions. Be sure to rinse and dry the thermometer before transferring it to a second solution. The solution temperatures should agree ±0.2°C. If they do not agree, you should use the average temperature as your initial temperature.

Measure out 50.0 mL of 2.0 M HCl and put it in the calorimeter. Put a stirring magnet in the solution, and set it moving gently (or stir gently with your thermometer). Measure out 50.0 mL of 2.0 M NaOH, add it to the acid, quickly cover and insert the thermometer. Record the temperature to the nearest 0.1°C after 20 seconds, and every 20 seconds for 3 minutes.

Repeat the procedure, combining solutions of 2.0 M NH_4Cl and 2.0 M NaOH, and for the third reaction combining solutions of 2.0 M NH_3 and 2.0 M HCl. Be sure that containers and thermometers are rinsed and dried between reactions.

Safety Alert

When NaOH and NH_4Cl solutions are mixed, ammonia gas is evolved. Work in a hood or under a funnel attached to an aspirator.

Calculations

1. **Calculate the Heat Capacity of the Calorimeter.**

   a. When equal volumes of hot and cold water are combined, if there is no heat loss the new temperature should be the average of the two starting temperatures. In actual practice, the new temperature will be slightly less than the average because of heat lost to the calorimeter assembly.

      Additionally, when two solutions are mixed the thermometer cannot instantaneously record the temperature of the combined solutions. The solutions require some time to become completely mixed, and the thermometer needs time to come to temperature equilibrium with the solution. The theoretical temperature that the mixture would have if the process occurred instantaneously can be found from a graph.

      Plot the data with temperature on the vertical axis versus time on the horizontal axis. The first few points may be erratic because of incomplete mixing and lack of temperature equilibrium with the thermometer. The points that follow should occur in a straight line as the temperature slowly drops while heat is lost to the calorimeter and to the surroundings. Draw a straight line through these points, and extend it back to find the temperature at time zero, the theoretical instantaneous temperature of mixing, T_{mix}. See Figure 1.

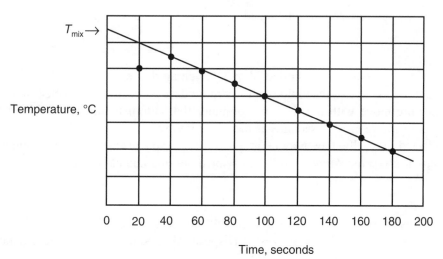

Temperature versus Time after Mixing

Figure 1. Graph to Find Heat Capacity of Calorimeter

   b. Calculate the average temperature of the hot and cold water, T_{avg}.

   c. The difference between the average temperature, T_{avg} and the instantaneous temperature, T_{mix}, is due to the fact that some heat was lost by the water and absorbed by the calorimeter. Calculate q_{water}, the heat lost by the water:

   $$q_{water} = \text{(grams of water)} \times \text{(specific heat of water)} \times (T_{mix} - T_{avg})$$

   where q_{water} = heat lost by water and the specific heat of water is 4.18 J/(g•°C).

   The heat absorbed by the calorimeter, $q_{calorimeter}$, will be equal to that lost by the water but opposite in sign.

   $$q_{calorimeter} = - q_{water}$$

   d. Calculate the heat capacity of the calorimeter, $C_{calorimeter}$, which is the heat that the calorimeter absorbs each time the temperature of the solution changes 1°C:

   $$C_{calorimeter} = q_{water} / (T_{mix} - T_{initial})$$

   where $T_{initial}$ is the initial temperature of the cool water.

2. Calculate ΔH for Each Reaction.

e. Graph the temperature versus time for each of the three reactions tested. Extrapolate the line back to find the theoretical instantaneous mixing temperature, T_{mix}, as you did above.

f. Calculate the amount of heat evolved in each reaction, q_{rxn}, by assuming that all of the heat is absorbed by the solutions and the calorimeter:

q_{rxn} = –[heat absorbed by solution + heat absorbed by calorimeter]

q_{rxn} = –[(grams of solution × specific heat of solution × $\Delta T_{solution}$) + ($C_{calorimeter}$ × $\Delta T_{solution}$)]

where $\Delta T_{solution}$ = (T_{mix} – $T_{initial}$) for each reaction mixture. Assume that the density of the solutions is 1.03 g/mL, and that the specific heat of the solutions is the same as that of water, 4.18 J/(g•°C).

g. Calculate the value of the enthalpy change, ΔH, in terms of kJ per mole of each reactant for all three reactions.

3. Verify Hess's Law.

h. Write net ionic equations for the three reactions involved. Show how you must arrange the first two equations to algebraically find the third.

i. Calculate the value of ΔH for the third reaction from your ΔH values for the first two reactions using Hess's law.

j. Find the percent difference between the calculated and measured values.

Technology

The temperature data can be conveniently collected by a temperature probe interfaced with a computer, or with a CBL® system. Using this type of technology allows more data points to be collected in a short time interval. Use a data collecting mode with the CBL or computer that automatically records both time and temperature. Record the temperature every 5 seconds as the solutions are mixed. Record for about 3 minutes. If the data values are collected manually, they may be graphed using a spreadsheet, or may be entered into a program such as *Graphical Analysis for Windows* and then printed out in graphical form.

Disposal

The solutions can be flushed down the drain with a 20-fold excess of water. Consult the *Flinn Chemical & Biological Catalog/Reference Manual*, Flinn Suggested Disposal Method #26b, or see the appendix of the teacher's manual.

Discussion

Include your data, calculations and answers to the following questions in your laboratory report:

1. What is meant by calorimetry?

2. How does the graphical temperature analysis improve the accuracy of your data?

3. The equation used to find the heat evolved in each reaction is q_{rxn} = –[(grams of solution × specific heat of solution × $\Delta T_{solution}$) + ($C_{calorimeter}$ × $\Delta T_{solution}$)]. What is the meaning of the negative sign in front of the bracket?

4. Do your values support Hess's law?

5. How could you modify the method to achieve greater accuracy?

6. Find a table listing standard heats of formation for the species included in your net ionic equations. Use them to calculate ΔH for each of these net ionic equations. Do these values support Hess's law?

34

Thermochemistry and Hess's Law

Preliminary Lab Assignment

Name_____ Date_____ Class_____

1. What is meant by ΔH?

2. Define specific heat.

3. The specific heat of a solution is 4.18 J/(g•°C) and its density is 1.02 g/mL. The solution is formed by combining 20.0 mL of solution A with 30.0 mL of solution B, both initially at 21.4°C. The final temperature is 25.3°C. Calculate the heat of reaction assuming no heat is lost to the calorimeter. Use correct significant digits.

4. In problem 3 above, the calorimeter used has a heat capacity of 8.20 J/°C. If you include a correction for the heat absorbed by the calorimeter, what is the heat of reaction?

5. State Hess's law.

Molecular Mass of a Volatile Liquid

It is often useful to know the molecular mass of a substance. This is one of the properties that helps characterize the substance. If the substance is a volatile liquid, one common way of determining its molecular mass involves using the ideal gas law, $PV = nRT$. Since the liquid is volatile, it can easily be converted to a gas. While it is in the gas phase, its volume, temperature and pressure are measured. The ideal gas law will then allow the calculation of the number of moles of the substance present:

$$n = \frac{PV}{RT}$$

where n is the number of moles of gas, P is pressure, V is volume, R is the ideal gas constant, and T is the temperature on the Kelvin scale. If pressure is given in mmHg, then $R = 62.4$ mmHg•L/mol•K. The number of moles of gas is related to the molecular mass, M, by the expression:

$$n = \frac{\text{grams gas}}{M}$$

The mass of the gas is found by first cooling the gas so that it condenses back into a liquid, and then determining the mass of the condensed liquid. The equations above can be combined into one equation that can be solved directly for molecular mass:

$$M = \frac{\text{grams gas} \times RT}{PV}$$

In this experiment to determine the molecular mass of a volatile liquid, some of the liquid is placed into a small test tube. The test tube is closed with aluminum foil that has a small hole in it. The test tube is heated in boiling water. The liquid vaporizes, the vapors fill the tube and excess vapor leaves through the hole. Since the tube is open to the air, the pressure of the vapor will be the same as the atmospheric pressure. The gas temperature will be that of the boiling water. The volume of the gas, which is the volume of the test tube, can be easily found. The mass of the gas must also be determined. To do this, the test tube is quickly cooled so that the vapor condenses back into a liquid, and the mass of the tube, foil and liquid are found using a sensitive balance.

Chemicals

Unknown volatile liquid

Equipment

Test tube, 13×100-mm	Beaker, 400-mL
Aluminum foil	Wire test tube holder
Thermometer	Hot plate or Bunsen burner, ring and wire gauze
Ice water bath	Analytical balance
Needle	Fume hood or funnel attached to an aspirator

Safety Alert

Vapors of the liquids used in this experiment should not be allowed to escape into the room. Work under a hood or under a funnel attached to a water aspirator. The liquid may be flammable or toxic. Check with your teacher to see if it is. If it is flammable, make sure that there are no open flames in the area.

Wear Chemical Splash Goggles and a Chemical-Resistant Apron.

Procedure

Trim a piece of aluminum foil so it just covers the top of a small test tube. Use a needle to make a small hole in the foil. Find the mass of the test tube and foil using a sensitive balance.

Pour about 0.5 mL of the unknown volatile liquid into the test tube, cover with the foil and immerse the tube in hot water in a large beaker. Use a wire test tube holder to keep the test tube submerged. Keep the foil above the water level. Heat the beaker of water to boiling, and keep at the boiling point while the liquid vaporizes. The expanding vapor will flush the air out of the test tube. As the liquid continues to vaporize, the excess vapor will escape out of the hole in the foil. The vapor will fill the tube at the boiling water temperature and at the room pressure. Keep the test tube in the beaker for at least three minutes after all of the liquid has vaporized. Measure the temperature of the boiling water.

Quickly cool the test tube in an ice bath, dry it off completely and find the mass of the test tube, foil, and condensed liquid.

Clean the test tube and fill it to the top with water, cover with the foil and find the mass of the test tube, water and foil.

Calculate the molecular mass of the volatile liquid.

Record the barometric pressure.

Calculations

Determine the mass of the condensed liquid.

From the mass of the water contained in the test tube and its density, calculate the volume of the test tube.

Use the mass of condensed vapor, pressure, temperature while in the boiling water bath and volume of the test tube to calculate the molecular mass of the liquid.

Disposal

See the *Flinn Chemical & Biological Catalog/Reference Manual*, Flinn Suggested Disposal Method #18a, or see the appendix of the teacher's manual.

Discussion

Answer the following questions in your laboratory report:

1. How can the ideal gas law be used to determine the molecular mass of a liquid?

2. Was the vapor really "ideal?" If not, how would this affect the calculated molecular mass? Be specific—for example, too high because…

3. Did all of the vapor condense into the liquid? Again, if not, how would this affect the calculated molecular mass?

4. Why is it not necessary to be precise when the liquid is measured out into the test tube?

FLINN SCIENTIFIC

Molecular Mass of a Volatile Liquid

Preliminary Lab Assignment

Name_____ Date_____ Class_____

1. The following data were obtained in an experiment to find the molecular mass of a liquid:

    Volume of gas: 8.23 mL   Temperature: 99°C
    Pressure: 742 mmHg   Mass of condensed liquid: 0.0326 g

    Calculate the molecular mass of the liquid.

2. The following mistakes were made when carrying out the experiment. What effect does each have on the calculated molecular mass? Be specific. For example, too large because…

    a. Only part of the test tube was immersed in the boiling water bath, so the temperature in part of the tube was less than that of the water bath.

    b. One milliliter of the liquid was initially placed in the test tube instead of the recommended 0.5 mL.

    c. The mass of the condensed liquid was not determined quickly. Instead, the test tube was allowed to stand for a while before its mass was measured.

3. List several other methods that can be used to determine molecular mass of unknown substances.

FLINN SCIENTIFIC

Molecular Mass by Freezing Point Depression

A procedure that allows the determination of the molecular mass of a substance is very useful to chemists. The molecular mass is an important value that must be known in order identify an unknown substance or to characterize a newly prepared compound.

There are a number of ways of determining the molecular mass of a substance. One of the simplest involves finding the change in the freezing point of a solvent when an unknown substance is dissolved in it. It has been found that the change in freezing point is directly proportional to the molality of the solution. This change in freezing point is one of several "colligative" properties of solutions—properties that depend only on the number of dissolved particles in solution, and not on the type of particle. Other colligative properties include change in boiling point, vapor pressure and osmotic pressure. Measurements of these properties can also can be used to find molecular mass of solutes.

The molality of a solution, m, is defined as moles of solute divided by kilograms of solvent:

$$m = \frac{\text{moles solute}}{\text{kg solvent}}$$

Since moles of solute is the same as grams solute divided by molecular mass of solute, M, then:

$$m = \frac{\text{g solute}}{\text{kg solvent} \times M \text{ solute}}$$

The relation to change in freezing point is:

$$\Delta T_{fp} = k_{fp} m$$

where ΔT_{fp} is the change in freezing point, k_{fp} is the freezing point depression constant for the solvent, and m is the molality of the solution. The value of k_{fp} must be determined for each solvent.

The equations are combined as follows:

$$M \text{ solute} = \frac{k_{fp} \times \text{g solute}}{\text{kg solvent} \times \Delta T_{fp}}$$

The solvent that will be used in this experiment is a nonpolar solvent with the common name butylated hydroxytoluene. This compound is abbreviated BHT and is frequently used as an antioxidant in foods. The IUPAC name for the compound is 2,6-di-*tert*-butyl-4-methylphenol. Its structural formula is as follows:

The freezing point of BHT is approximately 70°C. If the freezing point of both the solvent and the solution is determined using a thermometer which is calibrated every 0.1°C, the freezing point can be estimated in the range: ±0.01°C.

Figure 1 shows a cooling curve for a pure solvent and for a solution. Notice that supercooling may occur in both the solvent and the solution. If it does, as the crystals begin to form the temperature will rise slightly and then remain constant as the pure solvent freezes, or will slowly fall as the solution freezes.

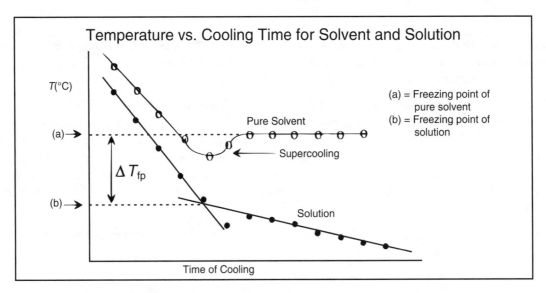

Figure 1. Freezing Point Graph for Pure Solvent and for Solution

Even though the melting point of butylated hydroxytoluene is known, it is necessary to determine it with the thermometer that will be used in the experiment. Thermometers can give temperature readings that are slightly different from true values. In this experiment we will be using the change in temperature to calculate the molecular mass. Even if the thermometer reading is slightly off, the change in temperature should be accurate. It is important that the same thermometer is used to determine both the freezing point of the solvent and that of the solution.

It is also necessary to measure the change in freezing point using a known solute in the BHT so that the freezing point depression constant can be calculated. Once this is known, the molecular mass of an unknown substance can be determined.

Chemicals

Butylated hydroxytoluene, BHT, $C_{15}H_{24}O(s)$ *para*-Dichlorobenzene, $C_6H_4Cl_2(s)$

Unknown substance

Equipment

Test tube, 18×150-mm   Thermometer (preferably graduated to $0.1°C$)

Beaker, large   Ring stand

Universal clamps   Wire stirrer

Cork or split rubber stopper with one hole   Hot plate or Bunsen burner, ring and wire gauze

Balance, sensitive   Weighing paper

Procedure

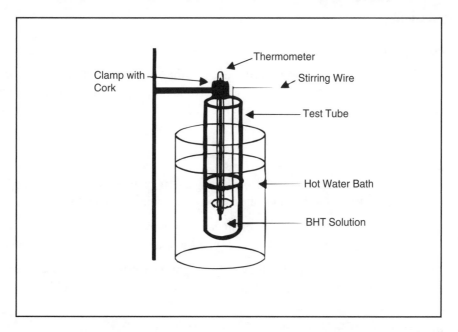

Figure 2. Diagram of Apparatus for Freezing Point Determination

Assemble an apparatus like the one diagrammed in Figure 2. Use a large test tube and a sensitive thermometer. Clamp the thermometer using a cork (not rubber) stopper which has a large hole, or a split rubber stopper. **Do not seal the test tube with the cork**—it is just to support the thermometer. Make a stirrer out of wire bent with a circle at the bottom. The test tube will be clamped in the beaker so that the solid it contains will be well below the level of the water in the beaker. Heat the beaker with a Bunsen burner or on a hot plate.

Weigh the test tube on a sensitive balance. Accurately measure about 8 grams of BHT into the test tube using a sensitive balance. Record the weight of the test tube and the BHT. Clamp the test tube in the water bath and insert the thermometer and stirring wire. Heat the water bath to about 90°C, remove the test tube from the hot water bath and record the BHT temperature every 20 seconds as the melted BHT cools. It is important to continuously stir the BHT to maintain even cooling. Stirring will also help prevent supercooling. Continue recording values until you have at least five which are constant. Make a note of the temperature where crystals begin to form. If time permits repeat this measurement.

Using a sensitive balance, accurately measure about 1 gram of *para*-dichlorobenzene onto a piece of waxed weighing paper and record its mass. Now place the *para*-dichlorobenzene into the test tube containing BHT. Heat the mixture in the hot water bath until the substances are all melted. Stir well to be sure that the solution is homogeneous. Again remove the test tube from the hot water bath, stir and record temperatures every 20 seconds until you have at least six values after crystals first begin to form. If time permits repeat this measurement.

Repeat the procedure using fresh BHT and about 1 gram of the unknown compound. If time permits repeat this measurement.

Disposal and Cleanup

Place the test tubes in a hot water bath until the mixtures are melted. Pour the melted substance out onto crumpled newspaper or paper towels. Consult the *Flinn Chemical & Biological Catalog/Reference Manual*, Flinn Suggested Disposal Method #26a, or see the appendix of the teacher's manual.

Rinse test tubes with acetone or ethanol before using detergent and water to clean them.

Graph and Calculations

Graph your data as in Figure 1.

Determine the freezing point of the solvent and each of the solutions, and the values of ΔT_{fp} from your graph. Calculate the freezing point depression constant from the data using *para*-dichlorobenzene. Then calculate the molecular mass of the unknown solute.

Technology

The temperature data can be conveniently collected using a temperature probe interfaced with a computer, or with a CBL® system. Using this type of technology allows more data points to be collected in a short time interval.

Use a data collecting mode with the CBL or computer that automatically records both time and temperature. Record the temperature every 5 or 6 seconds as the substances are cooled. Record for about 8 minutes.

If the data values are collected manually, they may be graphed using a spreadsheet, or may be entered into a program such as *Graphical Analysis for Windows* and then printed out in graphical form.

Alternate Microscale Procedure

Equipment

Capillary tubes	Beaker, 250-mL, or Thiele melting point tube
Thermometer with 0.1°C divisions	Small rubber band
Stirring rod	Ring stand, ring, wire gauze
Bunsen burner or hot plate	Sensitive balance
Beaker, 10-mL or 50-mL	Universal clamp
Mortar and pestle or watch glass and test tube	Cork or split rubber stopper

Procedure

Pulverize a small amount (about 0.5 g) of BHT. Use a mortar and pestle, or use a watch glass and the bottom of a test tube. Pack the BHT in a capillary tube to a depth of about 1 cm. To get the BHT into the capillary tube, push the open end of the capillary down into a small pile of BHT powder. Then turn the tube so the open end is up, and bounce the bottom of the tube on the desk top. You may also pack it by holding a long piece of 6 mm diameter glass tubing (1 m in length) upright on the floor, and dropping the capillary tube down the glass tubing so it bounces up and down a few times.

Cut a 1 mm length of rubber tubing to use as a rubber band, and with it fasten the capillary tube to a thermometer. The BHT should be level with the bulb of the thermometer. Use a universal clamp and cork stopper (or split rubber stopper) to fasten the thermometer to a ring stand. Immerse the bottom of the capillary and thermometer in a beaker of water (or a Thiele melting point tube filled with water) and heat. If using a beaker, you must stir the water to maintain an even distribution of temperature. You may heat rapidly in the beginning but as you get close to the melting point, heat very slowly in order to get an accurate value. Record the temperature at which the BHT melts (the white powder will become clear). If you wish to repeat the melting procedure, use a new sample and capillary tube.

Using a sensitive balance accurately measure about 0.5 g BHT into a small beaker. Then accurately measure about 0.1 g *para*-dichlorobenzene into the beaker. Heat the beaker gently over a small flame or on a hot plate. When the substance melts, mix it well with a stirring rod until it is homogeneous. Let it cool. After it solidifies, pulverize a small amount of it and find the melting point as you did for the pure BHT.

Repeat the above procedure using 0.5 g of BHT and 0.1 g of the unknown substance.

Calculations

Determine ΔT_{fp} for the solution of *para*-dichlorobenzene and of the unknown substance in BHT. Calculate the molality of the *para*-dichlorobenzene solution and use it to calculate the value of the freezing point depression constant, k_{fp}, for BHT. Use the calculated value of k_{fp} to find the molecular mass of the unknown solute.

Discussion

Include answers to the following questions as part of your laboratory report:

1. Give a definition of colligative properties.

2. Draw a phase diagram of a pure substance, and show how addition of a solute affects this diagram.

3. What is the least precise measurement? How does this limit your significant digits?

4. Why is it advantageous to choose a solvent that has a large value for k_{fp}?

5. Explain why the pure solvent shows a level horizontal curve as solidification occurs, but the curve for the solution slopes downward slightly.

Molecular Mass by Freezing Point Depression

Preliminary Lab Assignment

Name_____ Date_____ Class_____

1. The following data was obtained in an experiment designed to find the molecular mass of a solute by freezing point depression.

   Solvent: *para*-dichlorobenzene   Freezing point depression constant: 7.1°C/*m*
   Freezing point of pure solvent: 53.02°C   Mass of *para*-dichlorobenzene: 24.80 g
   Mass of unknown substance: 2.04 g   Freezing point of solution: 50.78°C

   Calculate the molecular mass of the solute.

2. The following errors occurred when the above experiment was carried out. How would each affect the calculated molecular mass of the solute (too high, too low, no effect)? Explain your answers.

   a. The thermometer used actually read 1.4°C too high.

   b. Some of the solvent was spilled before the solute was added.

   c. Some of the solute was spilled after it was weighed and before it was added to the solvent.

   d. Some of the solution was spilled after the solute and solvent were mixed but before the freezing point was determined.

Vapor Pressure and Enthalpy of Vaporization of Water

This experiment is designed to find the vapor pressure of water at temperatures between 50°C and 80°C. A graph of the logarithm of vapor pressure versus the reciprocal of absolute temperature allows the calculation of the enthalpy of vaporization.

A sample of air is trapped in an inverted 10-mL graduated cylinder which is immersed in a tall beaker of water. As the water in the beaker is heated to about 80°C, the air in the graduated cylinder expands and becomes saturated with water vapor. The temperature and volume are recorded. The total air and water vapor pressure inside the cylinder is equal to the barometric pressure plus a small correction for the pressure exerted by the depth of the water above the trapped air. The water in the beaker is allowed to cool. The volume of air contracts, and less water vapor is present at the lower temperature. The temperature and volume are recorded every 5°C between 80°C and 50°C. Next, the beaker is cooled with ice to a temperature close to 0°C. At this temperature the vapor pressure of water is so low that it can be assumed that all of the gas in the graduated cylinder is air.

The moles of air molecules in the cylinder can be found by using the volume of dry air present at the temperature near 0°C and the ideal gas equation. Knowing the moles of air in the container, the partial pressure of air can be calculated at each temperature, and the vapor pressure of water can be obtained by subtracting the pressure of air from the total pressure inside the cylinder.

The Clausius–Clapeyron equation is a mathematical expression relating the variation of vapor pressure to the temperature of a liquid. It can be written:

$$\ln P = \frac{-\Delta H_{vap}}{R\,T} + C$$

where $\ln P$ is the natural logarithm of the water vapor pressure, ΔH_{vap} is the enthalpy of vaporization of water, R is the gas constant (8.314 J/mol•K), T is the temperature (Kelvin), and C is a constant which does not need to be evaluated. It can be seen that this equation fits the straight line equation $y = mx + b$ where y is equal to $\ln P$, x is equal to $1/T$, and the slope, m, equals $-\Delta H_{vap}/R$.

If a graph is made of $\ln P$ versus $1/T$, the heat of vaporization can be calculated from the slope of the line.

Equipment

Thermometer, preferably ±0.1°C

Beaker, 1-L, tall form, or a beaker tall enough to immerse the 10-mL graduated cylinder

Graduated cylinder, 10-mL

Ring stand, ring, wire gauze, Bunsen burner (or hot plate)

Safety Alert

There are no particular hazards in this lab except for the care needed in handling the beaker of hot water.

Wear Chemical Splash Goggles and a Chemical-Resistant Apron.

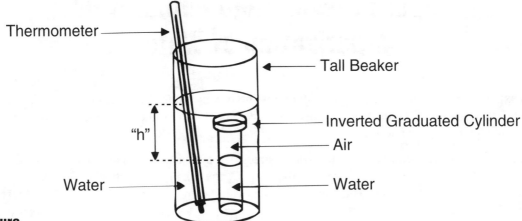

Figure 1. Diagram of Apparatus

Procedure

Refer to Figure 1. Fill a 10-mL graduated cylinder about 2/3 full of water. Close the top with your finger and quickly invert and lower the cylinder in a tall-form beaker half filled with water. Add water to the beaker until the water level extends above the cylinder.

Use a ruler to measure (in mm) the difference in height between the top of the water in the beaker and the top of the water in the cylinder, h.

Heat the assembly with a Bunsen burner or hot plate until the temperature is about 80°C. The air inside the cylinder should not expand beyond the scale on the cylinder. If it does, remove the cylinder (use tongs) and start again with a smaller initial volume of air. Record the temperature and the volume of air (±0.01 mL) in the cylinder. Be sure to continuously stir the water in the beaker to ensure an even distribution of heat.

Cool the beaker (continue stirring) until the temperature reaches 50°C. Record the temperature and volume of gas in the cylinder every 5°C. You may add some ice or ice water to the beaker to speed up the cooling slightly, but try to keep the volume of water in the beaker about the same.

After the temperature has reached 50°C, cool the beaker rapidly to about 0°C by adding ice. Record the gas volume and temperature at this low temperature.

Record the barometric pressure in mmHg.

Calculations

1. There is a small error in the measurement of the volume of air caused by using the upside-down graduated cylinder because the meniscus is reversed. Correct all volume measurements by subtracting 0.20 mL from each volume reading.

2. Calculate the total pressure of the gas in the cylinder from the barometric pressure and the difference in water levels between the top of the water in the beaker and the top of the water inside the flask, h. The pressure inside the cylinder is slightly greater than the atmospheric pressure and should be fairly constant throughout the experiment. This increased pressure can be calculated by using the measured difference in water depth, h, and multiplying by the conversion factor that the pressure exerted by 1.00 mmHg is the same as that exerted by 13.6 mmH$_2$O. This factor results from the fact that the density of mercury is 13.6 times that of water. We will assume that this correction is constant through the experiment. If the water depth is changed significantly, this calculation will need to be repeated.

$$P_{\text{cylinder}} = P_{\text{atmosphere}} + h(\text{mmH}_2\text{O}) \times \frac{1.00 \text{ mmHg}}{13.6 \text{ mmH}_2\text{O}}$$

3. Calculate the moles of trapped air, n_{air}, by using the volume of air present near 0°C and the ideal gas equation. At this low temperature we are assuming that the vapor pressure of water is negligible, so almost no water vapor is present in the cylinder.

$$n_{air} = \frac{P\,V}{R\,T}$$

4. For each temperature between 50°C and 80°C, calculate the partial pressure of air in the cylinder:

$$P_{air} = \frac{n_{air}\,R\,T}{V}$$

5. Calculate the vapor pressure of water at each temperature:

$$P_{water} = P_{cylinder} - P_{air}$$

6. Plot $\ln P_{water}$ (natural logarithm of water vapor pressure) on the vertical axis versus $1/T$ (1/Kelvin temperature) on the horizontal axis. Draw the best fitting straight line through the points. Determine the slope of the line, and calculate the value of ΔH_{vap} of water. Compare to the reported value for the enthalpy of vaporization of water.

Technology

The temperature data can be conveniently collected using a temperature probe interfaced with a computer, or with a CBL® system. Use a data collecting mode with the CBL or computer that automatically records the temperature and allows manual input of the volume. The data can then be graphed by the computer. If the CBL system is used, transfer the data to a program such as *Graphical Analysis for Windows* to graph and analyze it.

If the data values are collected manually, they may be graphed using a spreadsheet, or may be entered into a program such as *Graphical Analysis for Windows* and then printed out in graphical form.

Discussion

In your laboratory report, answer the following:
1. What is vapor pressure and why does it change with temperature?
2. What is enthalpy of vaporization?
3. The assumption was made that the vapor pressure of water is negligible at a temperature close to zero. Find the actual vapor pressure of water at your low temperature and comment on the validity of the assumption.
4. The assumption was also made that the slight changes in "h", the depth under the surface of the water, will not significantly change the total pressure in the graduated cylinder. Comment on the validity of this assumption.
5. Were your data values close to a straight line graph?
6. Write out the long "two-point" form of the Clausius–Clapeyron equation. Why does the graphical method of analysis give a better value for the enthalpy of vaporization than does the form of the Clausius–Clapeyron equation using two temperature–vapor pressure values?

Reference

Levinson, G. S. *J. Chem. Educ.*, **1982**, *59*, p 337

Vapor Pressure and Enthalpy of Vaporization of Water

Preliminary Lab Assignment

Name_____ Date_____ Class_____

1. A graduated cylinder containing some air is immersed in water as shown in Figure 1 in the lab directions. The height between the water surface and the top of the water inside the graduated cylinder is 106 mm. Calculate the correction that must be added to the barometric pressure to find the total pressure of the gases in the cylinder.

2. The following experimental values are for ethanol. Graph the data as shown in the experimental directions. Label the axes; draw the best straight line plot. Calculate the value of ΔH_{vap} for ethanol from the slope.

Temperature (°C)	Vapor Pressure (mmHg)	Temperature (K)	$1/T$ (K^{-1})	ln P_{vap}
10.0	23.8			
15.0	32.0			
20.0	44.1			
25.0	59.0			
30.0	78.6			

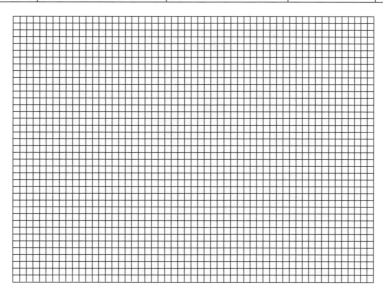

Show calculations:

Slope = _____ Enthalpy of vaporization, ΔH_{vap} =_____

Analysis of a Commercial Bleach

Many commercial products are effective because they contain oxidizing agents. Some products which contain oxidizing agents are bleaches, hair coloring agents, scouring powders, and toilet bowl cleaners. The most common oxidizing agent in bleaches is sodium hypochlorite, $NaClO$ (sometimes written $NaOCl$). Commercial bleaches are made by bubbling chlorine gas into a sodium hydroxide solution. Some of the chlorine is oxidized to the hypochlorite ion, ClO^-, and some is reduced to the chloride ion, Cl^-. The solution remains strongly basic. The ionic chemical equation for the process is:

$$Cl_2(g) + 2\ OH^-(aq) \rightarrow ClO^-(aq) + Cl^-(aq) + H_2O(l)$$

The amount of hypochlorite ion present in a solution of bleach is determined by an oxidation–reduction titration. One of the best methods is the iodine-thiosulfate titration procedure. Iodide ion, I^-, is easily oxidized by almost any oxidizing agent. In acid solution, hypochlorite ions oxidize iodide ions to form iodine, I_2. The iodine that forms is then titrated with a standard solution of sodium thiosulfate.

The analysis takes place in a series of steps:

(1) Acidified iodide ion is added to hypochlorite ion solution, and the iodide is oxidized to iodine.

$$2\ H^+(aq) + ClO^-(aq) + 2\ I^-(aq) \rightarrow Cl^-(aq) + I_2(aq) + H_2O(l)$$

(2) Iodine is only slightly soluble in water. It dissolves very well in an aqueous solution of iodide ion, in which it forms a complex ion called the triiodide ion. Triiodide is a combination of a neutral I_2 molecule with an I^- ion. The triiodide ion is yellow in dilute solution, and dark red-brown when concentrated.

$$I_2(aq) + I^-(aq) \rightarrow I_3^-(aq)$$

(3) The triiodide is titrated with a standard solution of thiosulfate ions, which reduces the iodine back to iodide ions:

$$I_3^-(aq) + 2\ S_2O_3^{2-}(aq) \rightarrow 3\ I^-(aq) + S_4O_6^{2-}(aq)$$

During this last reaction the red-brown color of the triiodide ion fades to yellow and then to the clear color of the iodide ion. It is possible to use the disappearance of the color of the I_3^- ion as the method of determining the end point, but this is not a very sensitive procedure. Addition of starch to a solution that contains iodine or triiodide ion forms a reversible blue complex. The disappearance of this blue colored complex is a much more sensitive method of determining the end point. However, if the starch is added to a solution which contains a great deal of iodine, the complex which forms may not be reversible. Therefore, the starch is not added until shortly before the end point is reached. The quantity of thiosulfate used in step (3) is directly related to the amount of hypochlorite initially present. The $S_4O_6^{2-}$ ion is called the dithionate ion.

Chemicals

Bleach, $NaClO$, commercial

Starch solution, 2%

Hydrochloric acid, HCl, 3 M

Sodium thiosulfate solution, $Na_2S_2O_3$, 0.100 M

Potassium iodide, $KI(s)$

Baking soda, $NaHCO_3(s)$

Equipment

Transfer pipets, 5-mL and 25-mL

Buret

Ring stand

Pipet bulb

Volumetric flask, 100-mL with stopper

Buret clamp

Erlenmeyer flask, 125-mL or 250-mL

Procedure

> ### Safety Alert
>
> Concentrated bleach is damaging to skin, eyes, and clothing. Hydrochloric acid is also hazardous. Both give off strong vapors. If you spill either solution on yourself, wash off with lots of water. Neutralize hydrochloric acid spills with baking soda.
>
> Adding hydrochloric acid to bleach may cause chlorine gas to be given off. *Carry out step 3 in a fume hood.*
>
> Always use a pipet bulb when pipetting. Never pipet by mouth.
>
> **Wear Chemical Splash Goggles and a Chemical-Resistant Apron.**

1. **Dilute the concentrated bleach.**

   Use a pipet bulb and a 5-mL transfer pipet to measure 5.00 mL of a commercial bleach solution into a 100-mL volumetric flask. Dilute to the mark with distilled water, stopper and mix well.

2. **Measure the potassium iodide.**

   Weigh out approximately 2 g solid KI. This is a large excess over that which is needed.

3. **Oxidize the iodide ion with hypochlorite ion.**

   Pipet 25 mL of the dilute bleach into an Erlenmeyer flask. Add the solid KI and about 25 mL of distilled water. Swirl to dissolve the KI. **Work in a fume hood** and slowly, with swirling, add approximately 2 mL of 3 M HCl. The solution should be dark yellow to red-brown from the presence of the I_3^- complex ions.

4. **Titrate the iodine.**

   Record the initial buret reading. Titrate with a standard 0.10 M sodium thiosulfate solution until the iodine color becomes light yellow. Add one dropper of starch solution. The blue color of the starch–iodine complex should appear. Continue the titration until one drop of $Na_2S_2O_3$ solution causes the blue color to disappear. Record the final buret reading.

5. **Repeat.**

   Repeat the titration beginning with step 2 two more times.

Disposal

The solutions may be safely flushed down the drain with a large excess of water.

Data and Calculations

1. Use the equations given to determine the number of moles of sodium thiosulfate that are equivalent to one mole of sodium hypochlorite.

2. Calculate the average volume of $Na_2S_2O_3$ needed for the titration of 25.00 mL of diluted bleach.

3. Use the average volume and molarity of $Na_2S_2O_3$ to determine the molarity of the diluted bleach.

4. Calculate the molarity of the commercial bleach.

5. Assume that the density of the commercial bleach is 1.08 g/mL. Calculate the percent by mass of NaClO in the commercial bleach.

6. Read the label of the commercial bleach to find the percent by mass NaClO that is reported. Calculate the percent error of your value, assuming that the label value is correct.

7. Calculate the average deviation of the three values you obtained for the molarity of the dilute bleach.

Discussion

Include answers to the following in your laboratory report:

1. Define oxidation and reduction.

2. Write balanced oxidation and reduction half-reactions for the equations (1) and (3). For each half-reaction, identify which substance is oxidized or reduced.

3. In this analysis, an "aliquot", or a diluted fraction of the initial solution is used for the titration. What advantage is there in diluting the original solution for the analysis?

4. How many 25-mL aliquots can be measured from a 100-mL volumetric flask? Explain.

5. The reaction with thiosulfate ions produces the dithionate ion, $S_4O_6^{2-}$. Calculate the oxidation number of sulfur in this ion. Do you think that the sulfur atoms in the ion will all have the same oxidation number? What might the oxidation numbers be?

6. How would each of the following laboratory mistakes affect the calculated value of the percent NaClO in the commercial bleach (too high, too low, no change)? Explain.

    a. In step 1, the pipet was rinsed with distilled water immediately before being used to measure the commercial bleach solution.

    b. In step 2, three grams of KI was used instead of two grams.

    c. In step 3, some of the iodine that formed vaporized from the solution.

7. What is the major source of error in this experiment? Explain.

Analysis of a Commercial Bleach

Preliminary Lab Assignment

Name_____ Date_____ Class_____

1. What is meant by a "titration"?

2. A solution of household vinegar (a mixture of acetic acid and water) is to be analyzed. A pipet is used to measure out 10.0 mL of the vinegar, which is placed in a 250-mL volumetric flask. Distilled water is added until the total volume of solution is 250 mL. A 25.0-mL portion of the diluted solution is measured out with a pipet and titrated with a standard solution of sodium hydroxide.

   The neutralization reaction is as follows:

   $$HC_2H_3O_2(aq) + OH^-(aq) \rightarrow C_2H_3O_2^-(aq) + H_2O(l)$$

   It is found that 16.7 mL of 0.0500 M NaOH is needed to titrate 25.0 mL of the diluted vinegar. Calculate the molarity of the diluted vinegar.

3. Calculate the molarity of the household vinegar.

4. The household vinegar has a density of 1.05 g/mL. Calculate the percent by mass of acetic acid in the household vinegar.

Determination of the Hardness of Water

Tap water contains a number of dissolved substances such as calcium, Ca^{2+}, magnesium, Mg^{2+}, iron, Fe^{3+}, carbonate, CO_3^{2-}, and chloride, Cl^-, ions. Those that prevent soap from forming a lather are the ions that give the characteristic of "hardness" to water. The two ions that are primarily responsible for hardness are Ca^{2+} and Mg^{2+}. Other ions such as iron, Fe^{3+}, also contribute to water hardness. The presence of these ions makes it difficult for soap to lather, and causes a "scum" to form with soap.

The amount of calcium and magnesium ions in water can be determined by the method of titration with a complexing agent called EDTA. Titration is the process of adding the exact amount of a chemical agent which is needed to react with substances dissolved in solution. The titrating agent is added using a buret, which makes it possible to accurately measure the volume added. In this experiment, the dissolved substances will be the calcium and magnesium ions, and the titrating agent will be EDTA solution. An indicator is used to determine the point at which all of the ions have reacted with EDTA. The concentration of EDTA must be known, and the volume of EDTA which was required for the reaction is measured. Based on the volume and molarity of EDTA, the quantity of the ions which cause hard water can be determined.

EDTA is an abbreviation for the chemical substance ethylenediaminetetraacetic acid which has the formula $C_{10}H_{16}N_2O_8$. EDTA is called a complexing agent because it has the ability to bond to ions in solution, forming a "complex ion". The large EDTA molecule literally wraps itself around the ions in solution. EDTA is often used to "complex" ions that may be present in solutions to prevent them from causing other reactions. For example, adding EDTA to hard water will allow soap to lather without forming scum. EDTA is sometimes used as an antidote in cases of poisoning by lead ions. The EDTA molecules tightly wrap around the lead ions in the stomach of the patient, and the lead passes harmlessly out of the body.

The structural formula of EDTA is as follows:

In a basic solution, the acidic hydrogens, that is the hydrogens attached to oxygen, are pulled away from the molecule. That leaves each of these four oxygen atoms with three nonbonding pairs of electrons and a negative charge. The two nitrogen atoms each have a nonbonding pair of electrons. The $EDTA^{4-}$ can bond to calcium or magnesium ions in six places: the four singly-bonded oxygen atoms and the two nitrogen atoms, each donating a pair of electrons to the metal ion. The resulting Ca–EDTA and Mg–EDTA complexes both have a minus two charge.

An indicator must be used to tell when the titration is complete. Eriochrome Black T, called EBT, is blue in basic solution. However, when EBT forms complex ions with Ca^{2+} or Mg^{2+}, the solution is pink in color.

During the titration the following processes occur:

1. Tap water containing Ca^{2+} and Mg^{2+} is placed in a flask. Some buffer solution, pH = 10, is added. The buffer maintains a basic pH so that the singly-bonded oxygen atoms in EDTA are not bonded to hydrogen atoms and can bond to the metal ions.

2. A small amount of EBT indicator is added. The EBT immediately bonds with some of the free metal ions forming a pink complex.

3. EDTA is now added from a buret. Initially, the EDTA will complex with the free calcium and magnesium ions present in solution. After all of the metal ions are complexed with either the EDTA or the EBT indicator, a "competition" occurs between the EDTA and the EBT for the metal ions. The formation constants for the EDTA and EBT complexes of Ca^{2+} and Mg^{2+} are given below:

Ca–EDTA	$K_f = 5.0 \times 10^{10}$	Ca–EBT	$K_f = 2.5 \times 10^5$
Mg–EDTA	$K_f = 1.3 \times 10^9$	Mg–EBT	$K_f = 1.0 \times 10^7$

The formation constants show that the strongest complexes are formed between EDTA and the metal ions. EDTA will begin to pull first calcium and then magnesium ions away from EBT. As the magnesium is removed from EBT, the indicator changes from the pink color of the Mg–EBT complex to the sky blue of EBT with no metal ion attached. This signals the end point of the titration.

Chemicals

EDTA solution, 0.0050 M

Buffer solution of ammonia and ammonium chloride, NH_3 and NH_4Cl, pH 10

Vinegar, $HC_2H_3O_2$

EBT indicator solution

Equipment

Erlenmeyer flask

Buret

Buret clamp

Pipet, 25-mL or 50-mL

Graduated cylinder, 10-mL

Ring stand

Beaker, 100-mL

Pipet bulb

Procedure

Safety Alert

The EDTA solution and the buffer solution are strongly basic. If you spill the solutions on yourself, wash them off with lots of water. Neutralize spills with vinegar.

The buffer contains ammonia and has a strong odor. Avoid breathing the vapors.

The EBT is dissolved in alcohol, so the solution is flammable.

Always use a pipet bulb when pipetting. Never pipet by mouth.

Wear Chemical Splash Goggles and a Chemical-Resistant Apron.

1. **Set up a buret.**

Obtain a buret and buret clamp. Clean the buret with detergent so that it drains without streaking. Rinse it with tap water and then distilled water.

Clean and *dry* a 100-mL beaker. Pour about 75 mL of the EDTA solution into the beaker to use as a supply to fill your buret. Pour about 10 mL of EDTA solution into the buret, and rinse the buret well with EDTA solution. Don't forget to rinse the tip as well as the barrel. Drain the solution, and repeat the rinse with another 10 mL of EDTA. Fill the buret above the 0-mL mark, and drain some EDTA with shaking so that the buret tip is filled and no air bubbles are present. The meniscus should be on the graduated part of the buret.

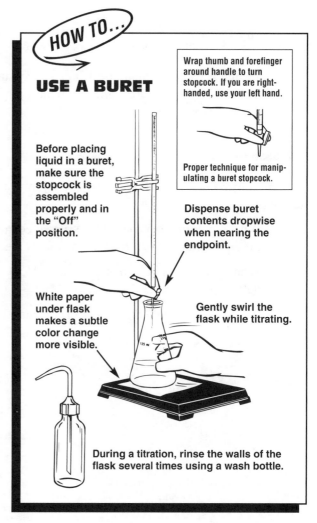

HOW TO...

USE A BURET

Wrap thumb and forefinger around handle to turn stopcock. If you are right-handed, use your left hand.

Proper technique for manipulating a buret stopcock.

Before placing liquid in a buret, make sure the stopcock is assembled properly and in the "Off" position.

Dispense buret contents dropwise when nearing the endpoint.

White paper under flask makes a subtle color change more visible.

Gently swirl the flask while titrating.

During a titration, rinse the walls of the flask several times using a wash bottle.

2. **Prepare the water sample.**

    Clean an Erlenmeyer flask and rinse it with distilled water. Pipet 50.0 mL of tap water into the flask. Add about 10 mL of pH 10 buffer solution and 5 drops of EBT indicator solution.

3. **Carry out the titration.**

    Record the level at which the EDTA solution is in the buret before you begin. Add the EDTA solution to the flask with swirling. When you get close to the end point of the titration, the pink color of the indicator will begin to turn purple. Continue the titration drop by drop until one drop of EDTA solution turns the solution sky blue. Record the final reading of the EDTA level in the buret. Since you don't know exactly when the end point occurs, this first trial may be done quickly to get an approximate value.

    Rinse the flask out with distilled water, and repeat the titration two more times to get the exact end point.

Disposal

The solutions can be flushed down the sink with a large excess of water.

Calculations

1. Find the average of the last two volumes of EDTA needed for the titration.

2. Use the molarity of the EDTA solution and the volume added to calculate the moles of EDTA required for the titration.

3. EDTA reacts with the hard water ions in a 1:1 mole ratio. Calculate the molarity of the ions present in the 50 mL of water tested.

4. Sometimes the hardness of water is reported as ppm Ca. This means that all of the hardness is assumed to be caused by calcium ions, and its concentration is reported in parts per million.

$$\text{ppm Ca} = \frac{\text{grams Ca}}{\text{grams solution}} \times 1{,}000{,}000$$

To find parts per million of calcium, convert the moles of metal ions present to grams of calcium. The density of water is 1.00 g/mL. Divide grams of calcium by grams of tap water, and multiply by 1,000,000.

Discussion

In your report, give all data and show how calculations are made. Include answers to the following questions:

1. What is a formation constant? Write an equation which shows the formation of Ca–EDTA and write the equilibrium expression that represents the formation constant.

2. What is a Lewis acid–base reaction? How does the formation of the Ca–EDTA complex fit this definition?

3. What is a "chelate"? Show how EDTA qualifies as a chelate.

Determination of the Hardness of Water

Preliminary Lab Assignment

Name_____ Date_____ Class_____

1. What is a complex ion?

2. Draw the Lewis dot formula of the $EDTA^{4-}$ ion that exists in basic solution, and indicate the non-bonding electron pairs that are used to bond with the metal ions.

3. An experiment to find water hardness required 18.2 mL of 0.0050 M EDTA solution to titrate 40.0 mL of tap water using an Eriochrome Black T indicator. Calculate the parts per million calcium present.

4. The value of the formation constant for Zn–Eriochrome Black R is 3×10^{12}. The formation constant for the Zn–EDTA complex is 3×10^{16}. Assuming that there is a visible color change between complexed and free EBR, can EBR function as an indicator for the EDTA titration of zinc ions? Explain.

Study of the Kinetics of a Reaction

This experiment is designed to study the kinetics of a chemical reaction. The reaction is called a "clock" reaction because of the means of observing the reaction rate. The reaction involves the oxidation of iodide ion by bromate ion in the presence of an acid:

$$6\ I^-(aq) + BrO_3^-(aq) + 6\ H^+(aq) \rightarrow 3\ I_2(aq) + Br^-(aq) + 3\ H_2O(l) \tag{1}$$

The reaction is somewhat slow at room temperature. Its rate depends on the concentration of the reactants and on the temperature. The rate law for the reaction is a mathematical expression that relates the reaction rate to the concentrations of reactants. If we express the rate of reaction as the rate of decrease in concentration of bromate ion, the rate law has the form:

$$Rate\ = \frac{-\Delta[BrO_3^-]}{\Delta t} = k[I^-]^x\ [BrO_3^-]^y\ [H^+]^z$$

where the square brackets refer to the molar concentration of the indicated species. The rate is equal to the change in concentration of the bromate ion, $-\Delta[BrO_3^-]$, divided by the change in time for the reaction to occur, Δt. The term "k" is the rate constant for the equation, and changes as temperature changes. The exponents x, y, and z are called the "orders" of the reaction with respect to the indicated substance, and show how the concentration of each substance affects the rate of reaction.

One purpose of the experiment is to determine the total rate law for the process. To do this we must measure the rate, evaluate the rate constant, k, and determine the order of the reaction for each reactant, the values of x, y, and z. A second goal is to determine the activation energy for the reaction. Lastly, the effect a catalyst has on the reaction rate is investigated.

To find the rate of the reaction we need some way of measuring the rate at which one of the reactants is used up, or the rate at which one of the products is formed. The method that we will use is based on the rate at which iodine forms. If thiosulfate ions are added to the solution they react with iodine as it forms in this way:

$$I_2(aq) + 2\ S_2O_3^{2-}(aq) \rightarrow 2\ I^-(aq) + S_4O_6^{2-}(aq) \tag{2}$$

Reaction (1) is somewhat slow. Reaction (2) proceeds extremely rapidly, so that as quickly as iodine is produced in reaction (1), it is consumed in reaction (2). Reaction (2) continues until all of the thiosulfate is used up. After that, iodine begins to increase in concentration in solution. If some starch is present, iodine will react with the starch to form a deep blue-colored complex that is readily apparent.

Carrying out reaction (1) in the presence of thiosulfate ion and starch produces a chemical "clock." When the thiosulfate is consumed, the solution turns blue.

In all of our reactions we will use the same quantity of thiosulfate ion. The blue color appears when all the thiosulfate is used up. An examination of equations (1) and (2) shows that 6 moles of $S_2O_3^{2-}$ are needed to react with the I_2 formed from 1 mole of BrO_3^-. Knowing the amount of thiosulfate used allows the calculation of the amount of I_2 that is formed, and also the amount of BrO_3^- that has reacted at the time of the color change. The reaction rate is expressed as the decrease in concentration of BrO_3^- ion divided by the time it takes for the blue color to appear.

This experiment is designed so that the amounts of the reactants that are consumed are small in comparison with the total quantities present. This means that the concentration of reactants is almost unchanged during the reaction, and therefore the reaction rate is almost a constant during this time.

The experiment is designed using a microscale procedure. Only 12 drops of reactants delivered from capillary droppers will be used for each measurement. The steps involved are as follows:

1. **Measure the volume of a drop of solution.** This must be done so that the number of moles of thiosulfate ion can be found, and so the amount of bromate ions that react can be calculated.

2. **Find the order of the reaction for each of the reactants, and calculate the rate law.** We will do this by carrying out an experiment at specific concentrations of each of the reactants and measuring the reaction rate. Then we will change the concentration of one reactant and observe how the reaction rate changes. This will be repeated for each reactant. This data allows the calculation of the order of each reactant. Once the orders are known, the value of the rate constant can be calculated.

3. **Determine the activation energy.** Reaction rates always increase as temperature goes up. By measuring how the rate changes as the temperature is varied we can determine the activation energy, E_a, for the reaction. The equation giving this relation is:

$$\ln k = \frac{-E_a}{RT} + \ln A$$

where $\ln k$ is the natural logarithm of the rate constant, E_a is the activation energy, R is the gas constant, 8.314 J/mol•K, and T is the temperature on the Kelvin scale. A is a constant called the frequency factor which we will not need to determine.

This equation follows the straight line relationship: $y = mx + b$. A plot of the natural logarithm of k versus $1/T$ will give a straight line graph. The slope of the graph will be $-E_a/R$, and we will use the slope to determine the activation energy.

4. **Observe the effect of a catalyst on the rate of the reaction.** The catalyst used will be $Cu(NO_3)_2$ solution.

Chemicals

Potassium iodide, KI, 0.010 M

Potassium bromate, $KBrO_3(s)$

Starch solution, 2%

Baking soda, $NaHCO_3(s)$

Sodium thiosulfate, $Na_2S_2O_3$, 0.0010 M

Hydrochloric acid, HCl, 0.10 M

Copper (II) nitrate, $Cu(NO_3)_2$, 0.1 M

Equipment

Beral pipets with capillary tips

Thermometer

Beaker, 10-mL or 50-mL

Sensitive balance

Trough for hot and cold water baths

Microplate, 12-well

Toothpicks for stirring

Cotton swabs

Procedure

Safety Alert

Hydrochloric acid is hazardous to skin and eyes. Wash off spills with lots of water. Neutralize spills on counter top with baking soda.

Wear Chemical Splash Goggles and a Chemical-Resistant Apron.

1. **Measure the Volume of a Drop of Solution.**

   Prepare Beral pipets with capillary tips from thin stem Beral pipets by stretching the stem close to the bulb. Cut the stretched section with a scissors. See Figure 1. (Alternatively, use micro tip Beral pipets.)

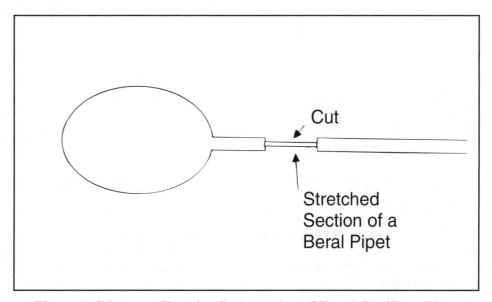

Figure 1. Diagram Showing Preparation of Beral Capillary Pipet

Place a small beaker on a sensitive balance and find its mass. Holding the dropper vertically, deliver 5 drops of water into the beaker, and find the total mass. Add an additional 5 drops of water, again determine the mass. Deliver 5 more drops and again find the mass. Record your data in a table in your notebook. See the Data and Calculations section for help in setting up your notebook.

Assume that the density of each of the dilute solutions that will be used is the same as that of water, 1.00 g/mL. Calculate the volume of 1 drop of each solution.

Hold Beral pipets vertically when you use them. Discard the first drop delivered, as it may contain an air bubble.

2. **Determine the Reaction Rate and Calculate the Rate Law.**

It is necessary to use consistently good technique to obtain reproducible data. Hold droppers vertically and be sure no air bubbles are introduced. Since such small quantities of reagents are used, it is very easy to repeat measurements. Practice your technique by carrying out the first experiment at least three times (more, if necessary) until your values are reproducible. Calculation of the orders of reactants are all based on the values obtained for the first experiment, so be sure to get reproducible data from the beginning. All other experiments should be carried out at least twice.

The table that follows shows the reagent quantities to be used in carrying out the reactions needed. Because we don't want the reaction to start until we are ready, *be sure the $KBrO_3$ solution is the last solution added*. It is important to use care in measuring out the solutions. Since the total solution volume is quite small, even one extra drop can cause a substantial change in concentrations.

Experiment Number	KI 0.010 M	H_2O	HCl 0.10 M	Starch 2%	$Na_2S_2O_3$ 0.0010 M	$KBrO_3$ 0.040 M
1	2 drops	4 drops	2 drops	1 drop	1 drop	2 drops
2	4 drops	2 drops	2 drops	1 drop	1 drop	2 drops
3	6 drops	0 drops	2 drops	1 drop	1 drop	2 drops
4	2 drops	2 drops	2 drops	1 drop	1 drop	4 drops
5	2 drops	0 drops	2 drops	1 drop	1 drop	6 drops
6	2 drops	2 drops	4 drops	1 drop	1 drop	2 drops
7	2 drops	0 drops	6 drops	1 drop	1 drop	2 drops
8	3 drops	1 drop	3 drops	1 drop	1 drop	3 drops

Table 1. Reagent Quantities for Experiments

A study of Table 1 shows that all experiments contain the same total number of drops of solution, 12 drops. Only one drop of sodium thiosulfate, $Na_2S_2O_3$, and one drop of starch solution are added to each well. In experiments 1, 2 and 3, the concentration of potassium iodide, KI, is gradually increased while all other volumes remain constant. Experiments 1, 4 and 5 have an increasing concentration of potassium bromate, $KBrO_3$. Experiments 1, 6 and 7 show an increase in the concentration of hydrochloric acid, HCl. Experiment 8 will be a test to see if calculated orders of reactants agree with experimental values.

Measure out the drops of solutions required for experiment 1 in one of the wells of a 12-well strip. *Be sure to add $KBrO_3$ last.* Stir the mixture thoroughly with a toothpick. This is very important, because it is impossible to achieve good mixing in the small well without stirring. Begin timing the reaction as soon as the $KBrO_3$ is added. Record the time required for the first tint of blue color to appear. Repeat the measurements until consistently reproducible values are obtained. Record the room temperature as the temperature of these reactions.

Empty the well plate, rinse with water and shake to dry the wells. Use detergent and a cotton swab, if necessary, to be sure the wells are clean and dry for each experiment. Carry out the experiments with solution volumes described in Experiments 2 through 8.

3. **Determine the Activation Energy.**

In this part of the experiment the reaction will be carried out at several different temperatures using the concentrations of Experiment 1. The temperatures will be about 40°C, 20°C, 10°C, and 0°C. Use your value for Experiment 1 at room temperature for one of these measurements.

Prepare a shallow warm water bath of about 40°C in a trough. Repeat the procedure using the concentrations in Experiment 1. Mix all of the solutions except $KBrO_3$ and place the well plate in the warm water bath. Also place the Beral pipet containing $KBrO_3$ in the water bath for at least five minutes. Add the 2 drops of $KBrO_3$ to the well, stir and time the reaction until the blue color first appears. Leave the well strip in the water bath while you are timing the reaction. It is not necessary to repeat with mixtures of Experiments 2 through 8.

Repeat with the quantities from Experiment 1 for each of the other temperatures listed above. Record the time of reaction and the temperature for each.

4. **Observe the Effect of a Catalyst on the Rate.**

Repeat the procedure of Experiment 1, but this time add 1 drop of 0.1 M copper(II) nitrate solution, $Cu(NO_3)_2$, and only 3 drops of water to the mixture. The total volume will still be 12 drops. Record the reaction time.

Technology

A spreadsheet or graphing program can be used to draw the graph to determine activation energy.

Disposal and Cleanup

The solutions can be washed down the drain with a 20-fold excess of water. Clean the well plates with detergent and water using a cotton swab.

Data and Calculations

1. **Find the Volume of a Drop of Solution.**

Set up a table like the one below in your laboratory notebook in which you can record the necessary data and calculated values. **Show a sample of each type of calculation.**

(a) Mass of empty beaker   _____

(b) Mass of beaker plus 5 drops water   _____

    (b) – (a) Mass of first 5 drops water   _____

Average mass of 1 drop of water   _____

(c) Mass of beaker plus 10 drops water   _____

    (c) – (b) Mass of second 5 drops water   _____

Average mass of 1 drop of water   _____

(d) Mass of beaker plus 15 drops water   _____

    (d) – (c) Mass of third 5 drops water   _____

Average mass of 1 drop of water   _____

Average of masses of 1 drop of water   _____

     Volume of 1 drop: _____

2.   **Determine the Reaction Rate and Calculate the Rate Law.**

In your laboratory notebook, set up a table similar to the one below in which you can record your data and show results of calculations. You should also include a sample of each type of calculation.

	Time, s					Temp. °C	Reaction Rate M/s	Initial Concentrations, M		
	Trial 1	Trial 2	Trial 3	Trial 4	Average			$[I^-]$	$[BrO_3^-]$	$[H^+]$
Exp. 1										
Exp. 2										
Exp. 3										
Exp. 4										
Exp. 5										
Exp. 6										
Exp. 7										
Exp. 8										

Calculate the Rate.

The rate will be expressed as $-\Delta[BrO_3^-]/\Delta t$. In each reaction there is 1 drop of 0.0010 M $Na_2S_2O_3$ solution. Calculate the number of moles of $Na_2S_2O_3$ present in 1 drop:

$$\text{Volume of 1 drop (in L)} \times 0.0010 \text{ mol } Na_2S_2O_3/L = \text{ moles } S_2O_3^{2-} \text{ ions}$$

The blue color begins to appear when all the thiosulfate ion is consumed. Examination of equations (1) and (2) allows us to calculate the moles of BrO_3^- which react as all of the $S_2O_3^{2-}$ ion is used up:

$$\text{mol } S_2O_3^{2-} \times \frac{1 \text{ mol } I_2}{2 \text{ mol } S_2O_3^{2-}} \times \frac{1 \text{ mol } BrO_3^-}{3 \text{ mol } I_2} = \text{ mol } BrO_3^- \text{ reacted}$$

The value of $-\Delta[BrO_3^-]$ in all reactions, since all experiments have a total volume of 12 drops is:

$$-\Delta[BrO_3^-] = \frac{\text{mol } BrO_3^- \text{ reacted}}{\text{volume of 12 drops}}$$

The rate of each reaction can be found by dividing $-\Delta[BrO_3^-]$ by the number of seconds required for the reaction to take place.

Calculate Initial Concentrations.

Calculate the initial concentration of each reactant for each experiment. This will not be the same as the concentration of the starting solution because combining the reactants dilutes all of the solutions. On dilution, the number of moles of reactant stays the same, therefore:

$$\text{no. moles } = V_{concentrated} \times M_{concentrated} = V_{dilute} \times M_{dilute}$$

where $V_{concentrated}$ and $M_{concentrated}$ are the volume and molarity of the starting, concentrated solutions, and V_{dilute} and M_{dilute} are the volume and molarity of the diluted reaction mixtures. Since volumes will be proportional to the number of drops of solution used we can substitute drops for volume.

For example, in Experiment 1 the initial [I⁻] is found in this way:

$$[I^-] = \frac{2 \text{ drops} \times 0.010 \text{ M KI}}{12 \text{ drops solution}} = 0.0017 \text{ M}$$

Find the initial concentration of each reactant.

Calculate the Order of Each Reactant.

Next we need to find the values for the exponents *x*, *y*, and *z*. The experiment is designed so that the concentration of one ion changes while the others remain constant. Comparing values in Experiments 1, 2 and 3 we see that Experiment 2 has 2 times the I⁻ concentration as Experiment 1, and Experiment 3 has 3 times the I⁻ concentration as Experiment 1.

Substitute the values for Experiments 1 and 2 into the equation:

$$\text{Rate} = k[I^-]^x \, [BrO_3^-]^y \, [H^+]^z$$

Exp. 1 Rate_1 _____ $= k\,[\quad]^x\,[\quad]^y\,[\quad]^z$

Exp. 2 Rate_2 _____ $= k\,[\quad]^x\,[\quad]^y\,[\quad]^z$

Divide the first equation by the second. Notice that most of the terms will cancel out and you will have:

$$\frac{\text{Rate}_1 \text{_____}}{\text{Rate}_2 \text{_____}} = \frac{[\quad]^x}{[\quad]^x}$$

> **Note:**
>
> To solve for an exponential value, take the logarithm of both sides of the equation.
>
> For example: $8 = 2^n$. $\log 8 = n \log 2$. $n = \log 8/\log 2 = 3$.

Divide and solve for *x*. Report the value of *x* to the nearest integer. Repeat the calculations using Experiments 1 and 3 to confirm your value for *x*.

Next use the same procedure with Experiments 1, 4 and 5 to find the value of *y*. Lastly, use Experiments 1, 6 and 7 to find the value of *z*. Show how your calculations are carried out.

Find the Rate Constant.

Substitute data from each experiment into the rate law equation to find the value of *k*. Report the average value of *k*. Don't forget to include proper units for *k*.

Experiment	1	2	3	4	5	6	7
Value of *k*	____	____	____	____	____	____	____

Average value: _____

Write the experimentally determined rate law.

Experiment 8 is a check on your data. Substitute the concentrations of the reactants for this experiment into the rate law that you determined and calculate the value of the rate of reaction. How does this calculated rate compare with the measured rate for Experiment 8?

Calculated Rate = $k\,[I^-]^x\,[BrO_3^-]^y\,[H^+]^z$ = _____

Measured Rate =   _____

% Difference =   _____

Show your calculations.

3. **Determine the Activation Energy.**

    In your laboratory notebook, set up a table similar to the following one in which you can record your data. Give a sample of each type of calculation.

				Time of reaction, s					
Approximate temperature °C	Measured temperature °C	Temperature K	1/Temperature K^{-1}	Trial 1	Trial 2	Average Time	Rate of Reaction M/s	Rate Constant, k (with units)	Natural Log k

Graph the data with natural logarithm of the rate constant, k, on the vertical axis versus $1/T$ (temperature in the Kelvin scale) on the horizontal axis. Draw the straight line that is closest to the most points, and find the slope of the line. The slope = $-E_a/R$, where E_a is the activation energy and R = 8.314 J/mol•K. Calculate the activation energy for the reaction.

4. **Observe the Effect of a Catalyst on the Rate.**

    Record the time required for the reaction to occur with and without the catalyst.

Discussion

In your discussion include answers to the following questions:

1. Why does reaction rate change as concentration changes?

2. Explain the procedure used to find the rate law.

3. Comment on the agreement between measured and calculated rates for Experiment 8.

4. Why does reaction rate change as temperature changes?

5. Explain the procedure used to determine the activation energy.

6. Differentiate between reaction rate and specific rate constant.

7. Comment on the effect of the catalyst. How would you expect the activation energy to change when a catalyst is added to the reaction?

8. Write out the "two-point" form of the Arrhenius equation which relates rate constants, temperatures and activation energy.

9. Make a general statement about the consistency of your data as shown by calculating the orders of reactants, and by the graphical analysis which leads to activation energy. Were the calculated orders close to integers? Did the check of the order give the same value for the order? Were the points on the graph close to a straight line?

10. How could you improve the data?

Study of the Kinetics of a Reaction

Preliminary Lab Assignment

Name_____ Date_____ Class_____

1. An experiment is designed to study the rate of the reaction: $2\,NO(g) + O_2(g) \rightarrow 2\,NO_2(g)$

Exp. No.	$[NO]_{initial}$	$[O_2]_{initial}$	$-\Delta[NO]/\Delta t_{initial}$
1	0.0125 M	0.0250 M	0.0282 M/s
2	0.0250 M	0.0250 M	0.112 M/s
3	0.0125 M	0.0500 M	0.0560 M/s

Write the rate law including the value for the specific rate constant, k.

2. The following data are for the decomposition of $N_2O_5(g)$. Graph the data as described in the experimental directions. Determine the slope. Calculate the energy of activation.

Temperature	Specific rate constant	Temperature (K)	$1/T$ (K^{-1})	ln k
25°C	3.7×10^{-5} s^{-1}	_____	_____	_____
35°C	1.3×10^{-4} s^{-1}	_____	_____	_____
45°C	5.0×10^{-4} s^{-1}	_____	_____	_____
55°C	1.4×10^{-3} s^{-1}	_____	_____	_____

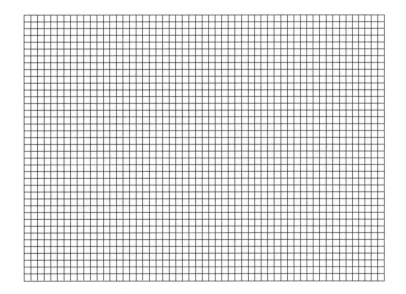

Show calculations for:

Slope _____ Activation energy, E_a _____

FLINN SCIENTIFIC

Determination of the Solubility Product of an Ionic Compound

The solubility product constant, K_{sp}, is a particular type of equilibrium constant. The equilibrium is formed when an ionic solid dissolves in water to form a saturated solution. The equilibrium exists between the aqueous ions and the undissolved solid. A saturated solution contains the maximum concentration of ions of the substance that can dissolve at the solution's temperature. The equilibrium equation showing the ionic solid lead chloride dissolving in water is:

$$PbCl_2(s) \rightleftarrows Pb^{2+}(aq) + 2Cl^-(aq)$$

The solubility product expression is:

$$K_{sp} = [Pb^{2+}][Cl^-]^2$$

where square brackets refer to molar concentrations of the ions. A knowledge of the K_{sp} of a salt is useful, since it allows us to determine the concentration of ions of the compound in a saturated solution. This allows us to control a solution so that precipitation of a compound will not occur, or to find the concentration needed to cause a precipitate to form.

The solubility product which will be determined by this experiment is that of the strong base, calcium hydroxide, $Ca(OH)_2$.

Chemicals

Calcium nitrate, $Ca(NO_3)_2$, 0.10 M

Sodium hydroxide, NaOH, 0.10 M

Vinegar, $HC_2H_3O_2$

Equipment

96-well Microplate

Beral pipets with capillary tips

Procedure

Safety Alert

Sodium hydroxide is a strong base and is hazardous to skin and eyes. If you get any on yourself, wash off with large amounts of water. Neutralize spills on the counter with vinegar.

Wear Chemical Splash Goggles and a Chemical-Resistant Apron.

Note

Hold the Beral capillary droppers vertically when dispensing the drops. Make sure no air bubbles are in the pipet tubes. Discard the first drop as it may contain an air bubble.

1. **Prepare a series of diluted calcium ion solutions.**

    Arrange a microplate so that you have 12 wells across from left to right. Put 5 drops of 0.10 M calcium nitrate in well #1 in the first row. Place 5 drops of water in each of the wells #2 through #12 in the first row. Next add 5 drops of 0.10 M calcium nitrate to well #2. Use an empty Beral pipet to mix the solution thoroughly by drawing the solution into the pipet and then squirting it back several times. The solution in this well, #2, is now 0.050 M in Ca^{2+} ion.

    Use your empty pipet to remove the solution from well #2 and put 5 drops of this solution into well #3. Put the remaining solution back in well #2. Mix the solution in well #3 as before. Continue this serial dilution procedure, adding 5 drops of the previous solution to the 5 drops of water in each well down the row until you fill the last one, #12. Mix the solution in well #12, and discard 5 drops. Determine the concentration of solution in each well, and verify that the concentration of calcium ions in well #12 is 4.9×10^{-5} M.

2. **Combine with sodium hydroxide.**

    Place 5 drops of 0.10 M sodium hydroxide, NaOH, in each of the wells #1 through #12. When the sodium hydroxide is added to each well, the initial concentrations of the reactants are halved, as each solution dilutes the other. Use an empty pipet to mix each of these combined solutions by drawing each solution up into the pipet and squirting it back into the well; or mix thoroughly with a stirrer. Now the concentration of Ca^{2+} ions in well #12 is 2.4×10^{-5} M.

3. **Observe the precipitates and calculate K_{sp}.**

    Allow three or four minutes for the precipitates to form. Observe the pattern of precipitation. At one point the concentration of both ions becomes too low to have any precipitate form. We will assume that the first well with no precipitate represents a saturated solution. Calculate the concentration of Ca^{2+} ions and OH^- ions in this well. Using these concentrations, determine the solubility product, the K_{sp} of calcium hydroxide.

4. **Check using a dilution of sodium hydroxide.**

    To check your results, repeat the procedure but use a serial dilution of the NaOH. In a different row, put 5 drops of 0.10 M sodium hydroxide in well #1. Put 5 drops of distilled water in wells #2 through #12. Add 5 drops of the 0.10 M sodium hydroxide to well #2. Use an empty Beral pipet to mix the solution by pulling the solution into the pipet and then squirting it back several times. The solution in this well, #2, is now 0.050 M in OH^- ion.

    Continue the serial dilution to well #12, and then remove 5 drops from well #12. Add 5 drops of 0.10 M $Ca(NO_3)_2$ to each of the wells, and mix each with an empty pipet or stirrer. Again, determine the well where no more precipitate appears.

    Calculate the concentration of calcium and hydroxide ions in the first well where there is no precipitate, and again calculate the value of K_{sp}.

    Look up the accepted value for the solubility product of calcium hydroxide in a handbook and compare to your values.

Disposal and Cleanup

    Solutions can be safely flushed down the drain. Clean the well plates with detergent and cotton swabs.

Discussion

Include answers to the following in your laboratory report:

1. Write the equation for calcium hydroxide, $Ca(OH)_2$, dissolving in water, and write the solubility product expression.

2. Show how you calculated the values for the solubility product.

3. Explain how you determined the concentration of each ion in the first well where no precipitation appeared. Why is this the well that you use to find the solubility product?

4. How did the values obtained from the two trials compare with each other?

5. Do you think that this method will give values that are too low or too high? Why?

6. What would make the method more accurate?

7. Would your results be better if you averaged the concentrations of the last well where precipitation occurred with the first well where there was no precipitate? Is there any justification for doing this? Try it!

Determination of the Solubility Product of an Ionic Compound

Preliminary Lab Assignment

Name_____ Date_____ Class_____

The ionic compound silver chromate is not very soluble in water. It ionizes according to the following equation:

$$Ag_2CrO_4(s) \rightleftarrows 2\ Ag^+(aq)\ +\ CrO_4^{2-}(aq)$$

1. Write the solubility product expression for silver chromate.

2. If one has a solution of 0.10 M silver nitrate and it is diluted by a factor of 2, what is the new concentration?

3. The dilution of 0.10 M silver nitrate by a factor of 2 is carried out five times. What is the concentration now?

4. The value for the K_{sp} of silver chromate is reported to be 1.1×10^{-12}. In a saturated solution of silver chromate, the silver ion concentration is found to be 2.5×10^{-4} M. What must the chromate ion concentration be? Show your work below.

FLINN SCIENTIFIC

Determination of the Equilibrium Constant for the Formation of FeSCN^{2+}

There are many reactions that take place in solution that are equilibrium reactions; that is, they do not go to completion, and both reactants and products are always present. Examples of this type of reaction include weak acids such as acetic acid dissociating in water, weak bases such as ammonia reacting with water, and the formation of "complex ions" in which a metal ion combines with one or more negative ions. We will study a reaction involving the formation of a complex ion which occurs when solutions of iron(III) are combined with the negative thiocyanate ion.

The equation for the reaction is as follows:

$$Fe^{3+}(aq) + HSCN(aq) \rightleftharpoons FeSCN^{2+}(aq) + H^+(aq)$$

The product, FeSCN^{2+}, is a complex ion in which Fe^{3+} ions are combined with SCN$^-$ ions to form thiocyanatoiron(III) ions. It is possible to follow this reaction and calculate the equilibrium constant because the complex ion has a deep wine-red color in solution, and therefore its concentration can be determined using a spectrophotometer.

The experiment involves two major parts. First, a series of solutions of FeSCN^{2+} must be prepared in which the concentration of FeSCN^{2+} ions is known. A spectrophotometer is used to measure the absorbance of light of each of these standard solutions, and then a graph of concentration of FeSCN^{2+} vs. absorbance is prepared. This graph serves as a calibration curve which will be used to determine the concentration of the complex ion in solutions of unknown concentration.

Secondly, a series of solutions is prepared in which varying amounts of the Fe^{3+} ion and HSCN are present. The absorbance of each solution is measured in the spectrophotometer, and the concentration of each substance present is determined. These values are used to determine the equilibrium concentrations and equilibrium constant for the reaction. We will use several different initial concentrations of the reactants to determine whether the equilibrium constant has the same numerical value when the complex is formed under different conditions.

Chemicals

Iron(III) nitrate, Fe(NO$_3$)$_3$, 0.20 M, in nitric acid, HNO$_3$, 0.50 M

Iron(III) nitrate, Fe(NO$_3$)$_3$, 2.0×10^{-3} M, in nitric acid, HNO$_3$, 0.50 M

Potassium thiocyanate, KSCN, 2.0×10^{-3} M, in nitric acid, HNO$_3$, 0.50 M

Nitric acid, HNO$_3$, 0.50 M

Baking soda, NaHCO$_3$ (to neutralize spills)

Equipment

5 Test tubes, 18 × 150-mm, and test tube rack

4 Burets, clamps and stands, or pipets

Stirring rod

Spectrophotometer and cuvettes

5 volumetric flasks with stoppers, 100-mL

Procedure

> **Safety Alert**
>
> All solutions contain nitric acid which is very corrosive to skin and eyes. Wash spills off yourself with lots of water. Neutralize spills on the lab table with baking soda.
>
> Solutions are toxic; so wash your hands before you leave the lab.
>
> If pipets are used to measure solutions, always use a pipet bulb. Never pipet by mouth.
>
> **Wear Chemical Splash Goggles and a Chemical-Resistant Apron.**

1. **Prepare Standard Solutions.**

   Note: The complex ion $FeSCN^{2+}$ slowly decomposes in nitric acid solution. Do not prepare the solutions for this experiment unless you can measure their absorbance values within one hour.

   In order to know the relation between the absorbance of a solution and its concentration, it is necessary to prepare a calibration graph of the molar concentration of $FeSCN^{2+}$ vs. Absorbance. The problem associated with this is that since the reaction is an equilibrium reaction, it does not go to completion, and the concentration of $FeSCN^{2+}$ in solution is difficult to determine.

   We will "force" the reaction to go almost to completion by adding a large excess (over 1000 times that needed) of Fe^{3+} ions to a small quantity of HSCN. According to LeChâtelier's principle, this should cause the reaction to go essentially to completion. In these solutions we can assume that all the HSCN present has reacted to form $FeSCN^{2+}$, so the $FeSCN^{2+}$ concentration can be calculated.

   The test solutions will be prepared using a mixture of KSCN, $Fe(NO_3)_2$, and HNO_3 solutions. KSCN ionizes into K^+ and SCN^-, and in the presence of the H^+ ion supplied by nitric acid, the H^+ and SCN^- combine to form the weak acid HSCN. Since there is a large excess of nitric acid compared to KSCN, we can assume that all of the SCN^- will be in the form of HSCN.

   Use pipets to measure the KSCN solutions listed in the table below into 100-mL volumetric flasks. Dilute to 100 mL with **0.20 M** $Fe(NO_3)_3$ in 0.50 M HNO_3. (Alternatively, use burets to measure both solutions.) Be sure to use the more concentrated iron nitrate solution. Calculate the concentration of $FeSCN^{2+}$ in each flask, assuming that all of the SCN^- has reacted.

   Notice that all the solutions that are combined contain 0.50 M HNO_3, so the H^+ ion concentration in all standard and test solutions will be 0.50 M.

Standard Solution	KSCN, 2.0×10^{-3} M in HNO_3, 0.50 M	$Fe(NO_3)_3$, 0.20 M in HNO_3, 0.50 M
1	2.0 mL	98.0 mL (Fill the volumetric flask with the solution)
2	3.0 mL	97.0 mL (Fill the volumetric flask with the solution)
3	4.0 mL	96.0 mL (Fill the volumetric flask with the solution)
4	5.0 mL	95.0 mL (Fill the volumetric flask with the solution)
5	6.0 mL	94.0 mL (Fill the volumetric flask with the solution)

Table 1. Quantities of Reagents Needed to Prepare Standard Solutions

Generally, spectrophotometers are used as follows: Turn the instrument on and allow it to warm up for 15 minutes. Set the wavelength at 445 nm. With no light passing through the instrument to the phototube, set the percent transmittance to zero with the "zero" control. Handle cuvettes at the top so no fingerprints are in the light path. Polish cuvettes with a tissue. Place a cuvette which is about 2/3 full of distilled water into the sample holder and set the percent transmittance to 100% with the appropriate control (not the zero control). Fill a cuvette about 2/3 full of a test solution, place it in the spectrophotometer and read the absorbance. Consult the instrument manual for details on its use.

Measure the absorbance of each of the standard solutions at 445 nm, using distilled water as the reference in the spectrophotometer. If absorbance is difficult to measure precisely on the meter because it is in the high range where the numbers are close together, measure percent transmittance and calculate the absorbance for each solution. Absorbance = $-\log T$, where T is transmittance expressed as a decimal.

Plot molar concentration of $FeSCN^{2+}$ vs. absorbance as shown in Figure 1, and draw the best fitting straight line through the data points. Include the origin (zero absorbance for zero concentration) as a valid point.

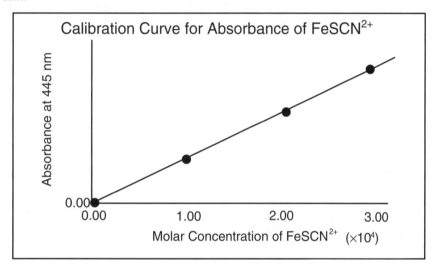

Figure 1. Graph of Absorbance versus Concentration of $FeSCN^{2+}$

2. Prepare and Measure Absorbance of Test Solutions.

The standard solutions contained a large excess of Fe^{3+} over HSCN. The test solutions will contain concentrations of Fe^{3+} and HSCN that are close to one another. Under these conditions, there should be fairly large percentages of all species present at equilibrium.

Use a buret or pipets to measure the quantities listed in Table 2 into five 18×150-mm test tubes. Mix the solutions well with a glass rod, and measure the absorbance of each at 445 nm, using distilled water as a reference.

Test Solution	2.0×10^{-3} M Fe(NO$_3$)$_3$ in 0.50 HNO$_3$	2.0×10^{-3} M KSCN in 0.50 M HNO$_3$	0.50 M HNO$_3$
1	5.0 mL	1.0 mL	4.0 mL
2	5.0 mL	2.0 mL	3.0 mL
3	5.0 mL	3.0 mL	2.0 mL
4	5.0 mL	4.0 mL	1.0 mL
5	5.0 mL	5.0 mL	0.0 mL

Table 2. Quantities of Reagents Needed to Prepare Test Solutions

Disposal

Consult the *Flinn Chemical & Biological Catalog/Reference Manual*, Flinn Suggested Disposal Method #24b, or see the appendix of the teacher's manual.

3. **Data and Calculations**

Standard Solutions

Prepare a table in your laboratory notebook like Table 3 in which you can record your measured and calculated values. Show an example of each type of calculation.

Solution	mL 2.0×10^{-3} M KSCN in 0.50 M HNO$_3$	% Transmittance (if needed)	Absorbance	Concentration FeSCN^{2+}, M
1	_____	_____	_____	_____
2	_____	_____	_____	_____
3	_____	_____	_____	_____
4	_____	_____	_____	_____
5	_____	_____	_____	_____

Table 3. Absorbance and Concentration of Standard Solutions

Record the absorbance of each solution. Calculate the concentration of FeSCN^{2+} in each of the standard solutions, assuming that all of the SCN$^-$ present is combined in the complex ion. Use the equation:

$$V_{concentrated} \times M_{concentrated} = V_{dilute} \times M_{dilute}$$

where V and M refer to the volumes and molarities of the solutions. Show a sample calculation.

Plot the data as suggested. Use a ruler to draw the best fitting straight line through the points. The point at zero absorbance for zero concentration is a valid point.

Test Solutions

Set up a chart in your laboratory notebook like Table 4 in which you can record your data and calculations. Show a sample of each type of calculation in your lab report.

Solution	(a) mL 2×10^{-3} M Fe^{3+} in 0.50 M HNO$_3$	(b) mL 2×10^{-3} M SCN$^-$ in 0.50 M HNO$_3$	(c) % Transmittance (if needed)	(d) Absorbance	(e) Initial moles Fe^{3+}
1	_____	_____	_____	_____	_____
2	_____	_____	_____	_____	_____
3	_____	_____	_____	_____	_____
4	_____	_____	_____	_____	_____
5	_____	_____	_____	_____	_____

Table 4. Data and Calculated Values for Test Solutions

Solution	(f) Initial moles SCN⁻	(g) Concentration FeSCN²⁺, M	(h) Moles FeSCN²⁺ at Equilibrium	(i) Moles Fe³⁺ at Equilibrium	(j) Moles HSCN at Equilibrium
1					
2					
3					
4					
5					

Table 4, continued. Data and Calculated Values for Test Solutions

Solution	(k) Concentration HSCN at Equilibrium, M	(l) Concentration Fe³⁺ at Equilbrium, M	(m) Concentration H⁺ at Equilibrium, M	(n) Equilibrium Constant K_c
1			0.50	
2			0.50	
3			0.50	
4			0.50	
5			0.50	

Table 4, concluded. Data and Calculated Values for Test Solutions

(a) (b) Record the volume of Fe^{3+} and SCN^- solutions in each test solution.

(c) (d) Measure the absorbance of each test solution. If the needle of the meter is in the high absorbance range, measure %T and calculate A. A = –logT, where T is transmittance expressed as a decimal value.

(e) Calculate the total number of moles of Fe^{3+} initially present in each solution.

(f) Calculate the total number of moles of SCN^- initially present in each solution.

(g) Use your calibration curve to find the concentration of $FeSCN^{2+}$ in each solution.

(h) Calculate the number of moles of complex ion, $FeSCN^{2+}$, present in each solution based on the concentration found in step (g) and the total solution volume.

(i) Find the moles of uncomplexed Fe^{3+} in each solution by subtracting the number of complexed moles of Fe^{3+} (h) from the initial moles of Fe^{3+} (e).

(j) Find the moles of SCN^- which are not complexed with Fe^{3+} by subtracting the number of complexed moles (h) from the initial moles (f). Since HSCN is a weak acid, the high concentration of nitric acid will cause any SCN^- not combined with Fe^{3+} to combine with H^+ and form HSCN.

(k) Convert the number of moles of HSCN found in (j) to molarity.

(l) Convert the moles of free Fe^{3+} found in (i) to molarity.

(m) Calculate the concentration of H^+ initially present in each of the solutions. The small amount of H^+ that combines with the SCN^- will not significantly change the concentration of H^+.

(n) For each experiment, calculate K_c for the reaction:

$$Fe^{3+}(aq) \; + \; HSCN(aq) \rightleftharpoons FeSCN^{2+}(aq) + H^+(aq)$$

$$K_c = \frac{[FeSCN^{2+}]\,[H^+]}{[Fe^{3+}]\,[HSCN]}$$

Calculate the average value of K_c.

Technology

The graph of the absorbance of the standard solutions can be made using a computer and spread sheet, or a program such as *Graphical Analysis for Windows*. The data can also be entered into a graphing calculator. In each case, the best fitting straight line graph can be determined using a linear least squares method, and the resulting values can be used to find the concentrations of the test solutions.

Discussion

1. In your laboratory report, show a sample of each type of calculation. Explain what is meant by an equilibrium constant. Was the value constant for all your experiments? Should it be constant?

2. What does the calculated value of the equilibrium constant, K_c, indicate regarding the degree of completeness of the reaction? In other words, at equilibrium, are there mostly products, reactants, or relatively large amounts of both?

3. When the calibration graph was prepared it was assumed that essentially all of the HSCN present was combined with Fe^{3+} to form the complex ion. Use the average value for K_c that you determined, and calculate the amount of HSCN that was not a part of the complex ion for the standard solution in which 5.0 mL of KSCN was used. Was the assumption valid?

4. Explain what a spectrophotometer is and what it measures. Describe how the "standard" solutions were obtained and used to determine concentrations of unknown solutions.

5. When you use a spectrophotometer, should you set the wavelength of light to be the same color as that of the solution, or would a different color be more appropriate? Explain. What was the color of light chosen for this experiment? What was the color of the $FeSCN^{2+}$ complex ion?

6. What degree of precision (how many significant figures) can you obtain with the spectrophotometer that was used? What is the major source of error in the experiment?

7. Suggest other experiments in which a spectrophotometer would be useful.

Determination of the Equilibrium Constant for the Formation of FeSCN^{2+}

Preliminary Lab Assignment

Name_____ Date_____ Class_____

1. Define equilibrium.

2. The reaction for the formation of the diamminesilver ion is as follows:

$$Ag^+(aq) \ + \ 2\,NH_3(aq) \rightleftarrows Ag(NH_3)_2{}^+$$

(a) Write the equilibrium constant expression for the reaction.

(b) An experiment was carried out to determine the value of the equilibrium constant, K_c for the reaction.

Total moles of Ag^+ present = 3.6×10^{-3} moles
Total moles of NH_3 present = 6.9×10^{-3} moles
Measured concentration of $Ag(NH_3)_2{}^+$ at equilibrium = 3.4×10^{-2} M
Total solution volume = 100 mL

Calculate the equilibrium concentration of Ag^+ (uncomplexed).

Calculate the equilibrium concentration of NH_3 (uncomplexed).

Calculate the value of the equilibrium constant.

FLINN SCIENTIFIC

LABORATORY NOTES

Determination of the Dissociation Constant of Weak Acids

When a weak acid is dissolved in water, it breaks apart or dissociates to a slight extent. A proton from the acid is donated to a water molecule. The equations for the equilibrium and the equilibrium constant expression are as follows:

$$HA + H_2O \rightleftharpoons H_3O^+ + A^- \qquad K_a = \frac{[H_3O^+]\,[A^-]}{[HA]}$$

where A represents the anion of the weak acid and the square brackets indicate molar concentrations of the species. For most weak acids the percent of acid that dissociates is less than 5%. The value of the equilibrium constant, K_a, indicates to what extent the reaction occurs. The greater the value of K_a, the stronger the acid, and the greater the amount of dissociation.

Polyprotic acids contain more than one ionizable hydrogen. The dissociation process occurs stepwise and there is an equilibrium constant for each of the steps:

$$H_2A + H_2O \rightleftharpoons H_3O^+ + HA^- \qquad K_{a1} = \frac{[H_3O^+]\,[HA^-]}{[H_2A]}$$

$$HA^- + H_2O \rightleftharpoons H_3O^+ + A^{2-} \qquad K_{a2} = \frac{[H_3O^+]\,[A^{2-}]}{[HA^-]}$$

The second reaction always occurs to a much smaller extent than the first, so K_{a2} is always a smaller value than K_{a1}.

Some values for K_a and pK_a ($pK_a = -\log K_a$) which cover a wide range of acid strengths are listed below:

Acid	Formula	K_{a1}	K_{a2}	pK_{a1}	pK_{a2}
Iodic	HIO_3	1.7×10^{-1}		0.77	
Sulfurous	H_2SO_3	1.7×10^{-2}	6.4×10^{-8}	1.77	7.19
Acetic	$HC_2H_3O_2$	1.8×10^{-5}		4.74	
Carbonic	H_2CO_3	4.3×10^{-7}	5.6×10^{-11}	6.37	10.25
Hypochlorous	$HClO$	3.0×10^{-8}		7.52	
Hydrocyanic	HCN	4.9×10^{-10}		9.31	

This experiment is designed to determine the K_a and pK_a values of a number of weak acids. Acetic acid, $HC_2H_3O_2$, will be used as an example for the experimental procedure.

When acetic acid is in water solution, an equilibrium exists in which a mixture of acetic acid, hydronium ions, and acetate ions will all be present:

$$HC_2H_3O_2 + H_2O \rightleftharpoons H_3O^+ + C_2H_3O_2^-$$

Acetic acid and acetate ions are conjugate acid–base pairs. A conjugate acid is a substance that has one more proton in its structure than its corresponding conjugate base. This combination also results from a mixture of a weak acid, acetic acid, and its salt, sodium acetate.

The equilibrium constant expression is:

$$K_a = \frac{[H_3O^+]\,[C_2H_3O_2^-]}{[HC_2H_3O_2]} = 1.8 \times 10^{-5}$$

If a solution contains equal concentrations of $HC_2H_3O_2$ and $C_2H_3O_2^-$, these concentration terms cancel out in the above equation so that $K_a = [H_3O^+] = 1.8 \times 10^{-5}$, and pH = p$K_a$ = 4.74.

We will prepare solutions in which the concentrations of acid and its anion are equal. The value of the pH of the solution will then equal the pK_a for the acid. Some of the substances tested will be salts of diprotic acids that still contain an ionizable hydrogen. For example, $NaHSO_4$ ionizes in solution forming Na^+ and HSO_4^-. The HSO_4^- then reacts with water in the equilibrium:

$$HSO_4^- + H_2O \rightleftarrows H_3O^+ + SO_4^{2-}$$

The value of K_a which is found when equal concentrations of HSO_4^- and SO_4^{2-} are in solution is K_{a2} for sulfuric acid, H_2SO_4.

Chemicals

Unknown acids

Phenolphthalein solution, 1%

Vinegar, $HC_2H_3O_2$ (to neutralize spills)

NaOH solution, approximately 0.1 M

Baking soda, $NaHCO_3$ (to neutralize spills)

Equipment

Beaker

Graduated cylinder

Dropper

Erlenmeyer flask

pH indicator paper or pH meter

Procedure

Safety Alert

Acids and bases are harmful to skin and eyes. Wash spills off skin with lots of water. Neutralize acid spills on the table with baking soda; neutralize base spills with vinegar.

Phenolphthalein is dissolved in alcohol, so it is flammable. Keep the solution away from flames.

Wear Chemical Splash Goggles and a Chemical-Resistant Apron.

Measure out a small quantity of the acid to be tested, about 0.2 g. It is not necessary to know the exact amount.

Measure precisely 50.0 mL of distilled water into a beaker, add the acid, stir to dissolve and mix well. Pour 25.0 mL of the acid solution into an Erlenmeyer flask. Add 3 drops of phenolphthalein solution to the acid solution in the Erlenmeyer flask, and then add NaOH solution dropwise while swirling the flask. Stop adding the NaOH when the first pink color persists throughout the solution for at least 5 seconds.

At this point the beaker contains exactly one-half of the original acid, essentially all of which is in the undissociated form, HA. The flask contains an equal amount of the anion of the acid formed by neutralization:

$$OH^- + HA \rightleftarrows H_2O + A^-$$

Pour the contents of the flask into the beaker and mix the solution. Using pH indicator paper or a pH meter, measure the pH of this solution which contains equal concentrations of weak acid and conjugate base. The measured pH is the pK_a of the acid. Calculate the value of K_a of the acid.

Disposal

The solutions may be washed down the drain with a large excess of water.

Discussion

In your lab report include answers to the following questions:

1. Assume the acid dissociation constant for the acid salt $NaHSO_4$ is to be determined.

    (a) Write the chemical equation to show this salt ionizing in water.

    (b) Write the chemical equation showing the anion acting as an acid in water.

    (c) Write the equilibrium expression for the acid dissociation of the anion.

    (d) Explain the procedure for determining the acid dissociation constant using the expression from (c).

2. Why is it not necessary to know the exact mass of the acid whose K_a is to be determined?

3. Why is it not necessary to know the exact concentration of the NaOH solution used?

4. Why is it necessary to precisely measure the volume of distilled water used to dissolve the acid?

5. Write the Henderson–Hasselbalch equation and show how it can be solved to find the K_a of an acid when the concentrations of conjugate acid and base are equal.

FLINN SCIENTIFIC

Determination of the Dissociation Constant of Weak Acids

Preliminary Lab Assignment

Name_____ Date_____ Class_____

For phosphoric acid, H_3PO_4, the values for the acid dissociation constants are:

$$K_{a1} = 7.5 \times 10^{-3}$$
$$K_{a2} = 6.2 \times 10^{-8}$$
$$K_{a3} = 4.2 \times 10^{-13}$$

1. Write the equation for the first dissociation of phosphoric acid with water.

2. Write the K_a expression for the above reaction.

3. What would be the pH of a solution when $[H_3PO_4] = [H_2PO_4^-]$?

4. Phenolphthalein would not be an appropriate indicator to use to determine the K_{a1} of phosphoric acid by the method used in this experiment. Why? What indicator would be appropriate?

5. What would be the pH of a solution prepared by combining equal quantities of NaH_2PO_4 and Na_2HPO_4? Explain with an equation.

6. Sufficient strong acid is added to a solution containing Na_2HPO_4 to neutralize one-half of it. What will be the pH of this solution? Explain.

Determination of the Equivalent Mass and pK_a of an Unknown Acid

In this experiment you will determine the equivalent mass of an unknown acid, that is, the mass of the acid that supplies one mole of hydrogen ions. The acid, a solid crystalline substance, will be weighed out and titrated with a standard solution of sodium hydroxide. From the moles of base used and the mass of the acid, you will be able to determine the equivalent mass of the acid. Next you will plot the titration curve of the acid, with pH on the vertical axis and the volume of NaOH on the horizontal axis. From this graph you will be able to determine the value of the equilibrium constant for the dissociation of the acid.

Acids are substances that contain ionizable hydrogen atoms within the molecule. Strong acids ionize totally, weak acids partially. The value of K_a, the equilibrium constant for the dissociation of the acid, is an indication of the strength of the acid. We can also speak of the pK_a, the $-\log(K_a)$, as an indication of acid strength.

An acid may contain one or more ionizable hydrogen atoms in the molecule. The equivalent mass of an acid is the mass that provides one mole of hydrogen ions. It can be calculated from the molecular mass divided by the number of ionizable hydrogen atoms in a molecule. For example: hydrochloric acid, HCl, contains one ionizable hydrogen atom; the molecular mass is 36.45 g/mole; the equivalent mass is also 36.45 g/mole. Sulfuric acid, H_2SO_4, contains 2 ionizable hydrogen atoms; the molecular mass is 98.07 g/mole; the equivalent mass is 49.04 g/mole. Thus, 36.45 g of HCl or 49.04 g of H_2SO_4 would provide you with one mole of H^+ ions.

The equivalent mass may be determined by titrating an acid with a standard solution of NaOH. Since one mole of NaOH will react with one mole of hydrogen ion, at the equivalence point the following relation holds:

$$V_b \times M_b = \text{moles base} = \text{moles H}^+$$

$$EM_a = \frac{\text{grams acid}}{\text{moles H}^+}$$

where V_b is the volume of base, M_b is the molarity of base, grams acid is the mass of acid used, and EM_a is the equivalent mass of the acid.

The concentration of the NaOH solution must be accurately known. To "standardize" the NaOH, that is to find its exact molarity, the NaOH is titrated against a solid acid, potassium hydrogen phthalate, sometimes abbreviated KHP. The KHP is chosen because it is easily dried and weighed, and has a relatively high equivalent mass. The formula of KHP is:

or $KHC_8H_4O_4$

It contains one ionizable H^+. The titration can be followed using phenolphthalein as an indicator.

A graph of pH versus mL of NaOH added can be drawn by carefully following the titration with a pH meter. There should be a significant change in pH in the vicinity of the equivalence point. Note that the equivalence point will probably NOT be at pH 7, but will be on the basic side. The value of the equilibrium constant for the dissociation of the acid can be obtained from the graph.

If we represent the dissociation of the acid as:

$$HA + H_2O \rightleftarrows H_3O^+ + A^-$$

the equilibrium expression is:

$$K_a = \frac{[H_3O^+][A^-]}{[HA]}$$

When the acid is half neutralized, $[HA] = [A^-]$, so these terms cancel in the above equation, and $K_a = [H_3O^+]$. Therefore, when the acid is half-neutralized, the pH = pK_a.

The point where pH is equal to pK_a can be found from the graph. Refer to Figure 1.

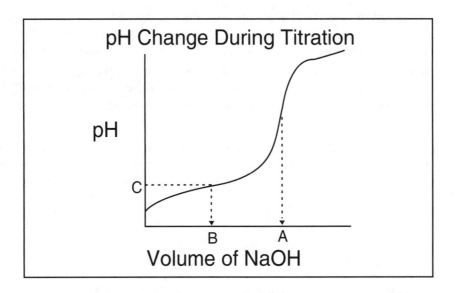

Figure 1. pH During Titration of a Monoprotic Weak Acid with Sodium Hydroxide

where

   A = Volume NaOH at equivalence point

   B = 1/2 volume of A or the volume when half-neutralized

   C = pH when half neutralized, or pK_a

If the acid contains two ionizable hydrogen atoms, the titration curve shows two separate inflections corresponding to the neutralization of each separate hydrogen. Figure 2 shows a titration curve for a diprotic acid such as H_2A. The dissociation of a diprotic acid can be written in two separate steps:

$$H_2A + H_2O \rightleftarrows H_3O^+ + HA^-$$
$$HA^- + H_2O \rightleftarrows H_3O^+ + A^{2-}$$

The two equilibrium expressions are:

$$K_{a1} = \frac{[H_3O^+]\,[HA^-]}{[H_2A]}$$

$$K_{a2} = \frac{[H_3O^+]\,[A^{2-}]}{[HA^-]}$$

If a diprotic acid is titrated, two inflections will be present if the pK_a values differ by 4 or more pK units. If this is the case, both pK_a values can be determined from the graph of pH versus volume of sodium hydroxide added. Refer to Figure 2 to see how this is done.

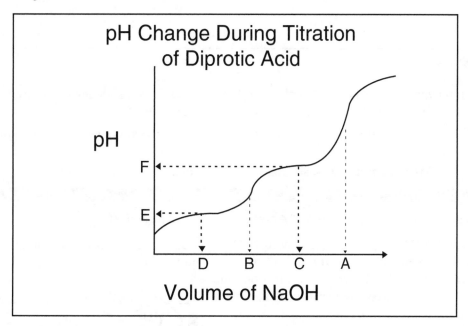

Figure 2. pH During Titration of a Diprotic Acid with Sodium Hydroxide

where

   B represents the volume of sodium hydroxide needed to react with one of the acid hydrogens
   A represents the volume of sodium hydroxide needed to react with both of the acid hydrogens
   D is the volume of sodium hydroxide needed to neutralize half of the first acid hydrogen
   E represents the pH when half of the first hydrogen is neutralized, or pK_{a1}
   C represents the volume of sodium hydroxide used when all of the first hydrogen and half of the
      second are neutralized
   F is the pH when half of the second hydrogen is neutralized, or pK_{a2}.

Chemicals

Sodium hydroxide, 6 M

Weak acid, solid

Buffer solution, pH 7

Baking soda, $NaHCO_3$ (to neutralize spills)

Phenolphthalein

Potassium hydrogen phthalate, $KHC_8H_4O_4(s)$

Vinegar, $HC_2H_3O_2$ (to neutralize spills)

Equipment

Bottle, 1-L	Balance, sensitive
Erlenmeyer flask, 125-mL or 250-mL	Weighing paper
Buret	Ring stand and buret clamp
Wash bottle	Magnetic stirrer (optional)
Beaker, 250-mL	Desiccator
Weighing paper	pH meter

Procedure

Safety Alert

Sodium hydroxide is caustic, hazardous to skin and eyes. If you spill any on yourself, wash off skin with lots of water. Spills can be neutralized with vinegar.

Phenolphthalein is dissolved in alcohol, so the solution is flammable. Keep it away from flames.

Wear Chemical Splash Goggles and a Chemical-Resistant Apron.

1. **Preparation and Standardization of Approximately 0.12 M NaOH**

   Since solid NaOH rapidly absorbs both H_2O and CO_2, a solution of exact molarity cannot be prepared by weighing the solid and diluting to volume. Instead, you must prepare a solution of approximately the desired concentration, and find its exact molarity by titrating it against a standard substance.

   a. Clean a 1 liter bottle and rinse with distilled water.

   b. Measure approximately 18 mL of 6 M NaOH, and dilute to about 1 liter with freshly distilled water. Use freshly distilled water so that the recent boiling has removed any dissolved CO_2 that would react with the NaOH.

   c. Mix very well.

   d. Obtain a sample of potassium hydrogen phthalate (KHP) which has been dried in an oven and stored in a desiccator, and use a sensitive balance to accurately weigh 0.4 to 0.6 g onto a piece of waxed weighing paper. Wash the KHP into an Erlenmeyer flask using distilled water from a wash bottle. Add about 40 mL of distilled water and swirl until completely dissolved.

HOW TO...

USE A DESICCATOR

Lubricate lip of desiccator and lid with stopcock grease to ensure a good seal

Desiccator Plate

Dry desiccant like Drierite® or anhydrous calcium chloride

A desiccator will provide an atmosphere with low humidity for the storage of samples, precipitates, crucibles and other equipment. Dessicants have a limited capacity to absorb moisture from the atmosphere. Learn how to tell when your dessicant is no longer effective.

Do not place hot items in a desiccator. As the items cool, they can create a partial vacuum in the desiccator and may spill when the desiccator is opened allowing the air to rush in.

e. Clean a buret, rinse it with tap water and then three times with small (about 7 mL) portions of your NaOH solution (don't forget to rinse the tip), and then fill it with your NaOH solution. Open the stopcock briefly and shake the buret vertically to remove air bubbles from the tip.

f. Add 3 drops phenolphthalein solution to the acid in the flask and then titrate with the NaOH until the first trace of pink color persists for 15 seconds. Remember to constantly swirl the flask, and to rinse the walls of the flask with distilled water before you reach the end point. Record the volume of NaOH used, estimating the nearest 0.01 mL. A buret reader may help you obtain precise readings.

g. Repeat two more times. If you use slightly more acid each time, the second and third titrations will be much more rapid than the first because you will know how much NaOH you can safely add before you get close to the end point.

h. Calculate the average molarity of your NaOH solution.

2. **Determination of the Equivalent Mass of an Unknown Acid**

a. Accurately weigh a sample of your unknown acid on weighing paper using the sensitive balance. You should weigh about 0.3–0.4 grams of the sample.

b. Dissolve in distilled water and titrate to the phenolphthalein end point as above.

c. Repeat one more time. Choose a mass for the second sample so that the volume of NaOH needed will be about 23 mL if you are using a 25-mL buret, or about 45 mL if you are using a 50-mL buret.

3. **Determination of the pK_a of the Unknown Acid**

a. On the analytical balance weigh a sample of your acid that will require approximately 20 mL of titrant if you are using a 25-mL buret, or 40 mL if you are using a 50-mL buret.

b. Dissolve the sample in approximately 100 mL distilled water in a beaker.

c. Set up a pH meter and electrode. Calibrate the pH meter as your teacher directs using a buffer solution of pH 7.00. Rinse the electrode well with distilled water.

d. Set the beaker on a magnetic stirrer if one is available. Clamp the pH electrode so it is submerged in your acid solution. Be sure the magnet does not hit the electrode. Titrate with standard base, recording the volume of base and pH of the solution during the titration. You should record the volume and pH every mL during the initial part of the titration, but as you get closer to the equivalence point, you must use smaller increments, approximately one drop in the vicinity of the equivalence point. Continue the titration curve at least 3 mL beyond the equivalence point.

e. Graph your data, with pH on the vertical axis and volume NaOH on the horizontal axis. Make your graph large enough to reflect the care you took with the measurements of pH and volume NaOH. From the graph determine the pK_a of the acid, that is, the pH where the acid is half-neutralized. If your acid appears to be a diprotic acid, give both pK_a values.

f. Calculate the K_a value (or values) of your acid.

g. Determine the volume of NaOH needed to reach the equivalence point. Use this value and each of the two values you recorded for the titration of your acid in part 2 to determine the equivalent mass of your acid. Average the three equivalent mass values, and determine the percent deviation.

Disposal and Cleanup

The solutions may be safely washed down the sink with a large excess of water. Be sure to clean the buret well and give it a final rinse with distilled water.

Technology

Part 3 of this experiment can be followed using a pH electrode interfaced with a computer, or a CBL® system. Use a mode of recording data in which the volume of NaOH is entered into the computer or calculator manually, and the pH is recorded automatically. For the CBL system this would be the "trigger–prompt" mode. The data can then be graphed by the computer (use a program such as *Graphical Analysis for Windows* if using the CBL system). Even though the graphing is done on the computer, it must still follow the guidelines given on page *viii*.

Discussion

In your lab write-up, answer the following questions:

1. What is equivalent mass? Why do we determine equivalent mass and not molecular mass?

2. What is a standard solution?

3. What is a titration?

4. Why must the KHP and the acid samples be dried? If they were not, how would your results change (high or low)?

5. What is pH? When the pH changes by one unit, how does the hydrogen ion concentration change?

6. Why is the equivalence point not at pH 7?

7. What is K_a? What does it mean? How is it determined from the graph?

8. Did your graph give any indication that your acid may have contained more than one ionizable hydrogen?

9. How precisely can you read a buret? The sensitive balance? Why is it better to titrate with a volume of base that fills most of your buret?

10. Use your calculated K_a value to determine the pH at the equivalence point. Compare this value to your observed value on your graph.

Determination of the Equivalent Mass and pK_a of an Unknown Acid

Preliminary Lab Assignment

Name_____ Date_____ Class_____

1. What is the equivalent mass of each of the following acids?

   a. $HC_2H_3O_2$ b. $KHCO_3$ c. H_2SO_3

2. Calculate the molarity of a solution of sodium hydroxide, NaOH, if 23.64 mL is needed to neutralize 0.5632 g of potassium hydrogen phthalate.

3. It is found that 24.68 mL of 0.1165 M NaOH is needed to titrate 0.2931 g of an unknown acid to the phenolphthalein end point. Calculate the equivalent mass of the acid.

4. The following values were experimentally determined for the titration of 0.145 g of a weak acid with 0.100 M NaOH:

Volume NaOH, mL	pH
0.00	2.88
5.00	4.15
10.00	4.58
12.50	4.76
15.00	4.93
20.00	5.36
24.00	6.14
24.90	7.15
25.00	8.73
26.00	11.29
30.00	11.96

a. Graph the data on the chart below.

Change of pH During Titration of Weak Acid with NaOH

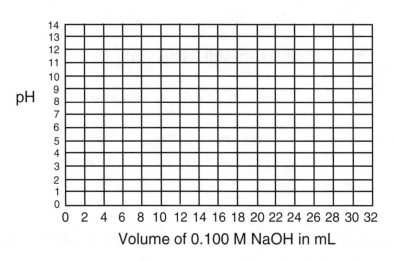

pH

Volume of 0.100 M NaOH in mL

b. What is the pH at the equivalence point?

c. Does the acid appear to be monoprotic or diprotic? Explain.

d. Give the K_a and pK_a value (or values) of the acid. Explain.

e. Calculate the equivalent mass of the acid.

f. The following acid–base indicators are available to follow the titration. Which of them would be most appropriate? Explain.

Indicator	Color Change		pH Transition Interval
	Acid Form	**Base Form**	
Bromphenol blue	yellow	blue	3.0 – 5.0
Bromthymol blue	yellow	blue	6.0 – 7.6
Thymol blue	yellow	blue	8.0 – 9.6

Equilibrium and LeChâtelier's Principle

LeChâtelier's Principle states that: If an equilibrium system is subjected to a stress, the system will react to remove the stress. To remove a stress, a system can only do one of two things: form more products using up reactants, or reverse the reaction and form more reactants, using up products. In this experiment you will form several equilibrium systems. Then, by putting different stresses on the systems, you will observe how equilibrium systems react to a stress.

Before you carry out each section, predict which way you think the equilibrium will shift. Then, carry out the reaction to verify your prediction.

Chemicals

Sodium chloride, NaCl(s)

Potassium thiocyanate, KSCN, 0.002 M

Bromthymol blue indicator solution

Potassium thiocyanate, KSCN(s)

Silver nitrate, $AgNO_3$, 0.1 M

Cobalt(II) chloride, $CoCl_2 \cdot 6H_2O$(s)

Hydrochloric acid, HCl, 12 M

Hydrochloric acid, HCl, 0.1 M

Sodium hydroxide, NaOH, 0.1 M

Iron(III) nitrate, $Fe(NO_3)_3$, 0.2 M

Ethanol, C_2H_5OH(l)

Disodium hydrogen phosphate, Na_2HPO_4(s)

Equipment

Test tubes, 13×150-mm

Beaker, 100 mL

Stirring rod

Test tube rack

Graduated cylinders

Funnel, filter paper, and holder for funnel

Procedure

Safety Alert

You will be using a concentrated solution of hydrochloric acid, as well as 0.1 M hydrochloric acid. Hydrochloric acid is hazardous. Use it with care. It has strong vapors. Avoid breathing them. Wash spills off yourself with lots of water. Neutralize spills on the lab bench with baking soda.

You will also be using 0.1 M sodium hydroxide. This is also hazardous. Wash spills off with water; neutralize spills on the lab bench with vinegar.

The alcohol is flammable. Keep it away from flames.

Wear Chemical Splash Goggles and a Chemical-Resistant Apron.

1. **Equilibrium in a Saturated Solution**

You will investigate the equilibrium in saturated sodium chloride solution:

$$NaCl(s) \rightleftarrows Na^+(aq) + Cl^-(aq)$$

Pour some solid NaCl into a 13- × 100-mm test tube and fill the tube 3/4 full of distilled water. Cork and shake to form a saturated solution. If all the NaCl dissolves, pour some additional NaCl in the tube and shake until a saturated solution with some excess solid is obtained.

Filter the solution into a second test tube. To this saturated solution of NaCl, add some Cl^- ions in the form of concentrated HCl. Record and explain the results.

2. **An Acid–Base Indicator Equilibrium**

Acid–base indicators are large organic molecules that can gain and lose hydrogen ions to form substances that have different colors. The reaction of the indicator bromthymol blue can be illustrated as follows:

$$HIn(aq) \rightleftarrows H^+(aq) + In^-(aq)$$

yellow   blue

In this reaction HIn is the neutral indicator molecule, and In^- is the indicator ion after the molecule has lost a hydrogen ion. Equilibrium reactions can easily be forced to go in either direction. Reactions like this are said to be reversible.

Fill a small test tube about half-full of distilled water. Add several drops of bromthymol blue indicator solution. Add 5 drops of 0.1 M HCl and stir. This will increase the amount of H^+ in solution. Note the color of the indicator.

Next add 0.1 M NaOH drop by drop with stirring until no further color change occurs. Adding OH^- ions causes the H^+ ion concentration to decrease as the ions combine to form water molecules. Again, note the color. See if you can add the right amount of acid to this test tube to cause the solution to be green in color after it is stirred (half of the indicator is blue and half is yellow).

3. **A Complex Ion Equilibrium**

An equilibrium system can be formed in solution with the following ions:

$$Fe^{3+}(aq) + SCN^-(aq) \rightleftarrows FeSCN^{2+}(aq)$$

colorless   colorless   red-brown

The iron ion (Fe^{3+}) and the thiocyanate ion (SCN^-) are both colorless; however, the ion that forms from their combination, the $FeSCN^{2+}$ ion, is colored a dark red-brown. It is the color of this ion that will indicate how the equilibrium system is being affected.

Pour about 25 mL of 0.0020 M KSCN solution (a source of SCN^- ion) into a beaker. Add 25 mL of distilled water and 5 drops of 0.20 M $Fe(NO_3)_3$ solution. Swirl the solution and note the following: the color of the KSCN solution, the color of the $Fe(NO_3)_3$ solution, and the color of the resulting complex ion.

You will stress the equilibrium system that has resulted in several ways. Pour equal amounts of the solution from the beaker into four test tubes. The solution in the first test tube will be the reference solution.

To the second test tube add 2–3 crystals of solid KSCN. Describe the results.

To the third test tube add 6 drops of $Fe(NO_3)_3$ solution. Stir and describe the results.

To the fourth test tube add small crystals of Na_2HPO_4, a few at a time. Stir and note the results. Phosphate ions, PO_4^{3-}, have the ability to form complex ions with Fe^{3+}, which has the same effect as removing Fe^{3+} from solution.

4. An Equilibrium with Cobalt Complex Ions

In this section we will investigate the equilibrium between two different complex ions of cobalt. The reaction is endothermic:

$$Co(H_2O)_6^{2+}(aq) + 4\,Cl^-(aq) \rightleftarrows CoCl_4^{2-}(aq) + 6\,H_2O(l) \quad \Delta H = +50 \text{ kJ/mol}$$

      pink   blue

Safety Alert

Ethanol is flammable. Turn off all flames.

Silver nitrate causes stains on skin and clothing. Wash spills off with soap and water immediately.

Measure about 10 mL of ethanol into a beaker.

Examine solid cobalt(II) chloride, noting both its color and the formula of the compound. Dissolve a small amount of cobalt(II) chloride (about half the size of a pea) in the beaker of ethanol. The solution should be purple. If it is pink, add a little concentrated HCl until it is purple.

Put about 2 mL of the alcoholic cobalt solution into each of three small test tubes. To one of the test tubes, add 3 drops of distilled water, one drop at a time with stirring, noting what happens with each drop. Add 3 drops of distilled water to each of the other two test tubes. Make a note of the effect of this stress on the system.

The first test tube is the control. To the second test tube, add 5 drops of concentrated HCl, 12 M, one drop at a time with stirring. Note the results.

To the third test tube add a few crystals of solid sodium chloride. Stir and note the results.

Put the remainder of alcoholic cobalt solution from the beaker into a fourth test tube. Add 10 drops of 0.1 M silver nitrate solution, one drop at a time. Silver and chloride ions combine to form a precipitate of AgCl. Note the color of the solution as the chloride ions precipitate. You may wish to let the precipitate settle to observe the solution color more easily, or you may centrifuge the test tube.

Obtain a sealed Beral pipet containing some of the alcoholic cobalt chloride–water system. Note its color. Immerse the large end of the pipet in some hot water (about 60°C) and see if there is a color change.

Lastly, chill the Beral pipet in an ice bath to see if the color change in the previous step is reversible. Explain the effect of the temperature change on the equilibrium in terms of the fact that the value of ΔH for the reaction is +50 kJ/mol.

Disposal

Solutions from Parts 1, 2 and 3 can be safely washed down the sink with excess water. Dispose of the solutions containing cobalt from Part 4 according to the *Flinn Chemical & Biological Catalog/Reference Manual*, Flinn Suggested Disposal Method #27f, or see the appendix of the teacher's manual.

Discussion

In your laboratory manual describe the results of each part of the experiment and interpret them using LeChâtelier's Principle.

Equilibrium and LeChâtelier's Principle

Preliminary Lab Assignment

Name_____ Date_____ Class_____

1. Define equilibrium.

2. State LeChâtelier's Principle.

3. $6\ CO_2(g)\ +\ 6\ H_2O(l)\ \rightleftarrows\ C_6H_{12}O_6(s)\ +\ 6\ O_2(g)$ $\Delta H = 2820\ kJ$

    For the above reaction tell how the amount of $C_6H_{12}O_6(s)$ present at equilibrium would be affected by each of the following:

    (a) Some $CO_2(g)$ is added.

    (b) The temperature is raised.

    (c) The volume is decreased.

    (d) Some $O_2(g)$ is removed.

    (e) Some of the $C_6H_{12}O_6(s)$ is removed.

    (f) A catalyst is added.

    (g) Some H_2O is removed.

FLINN SCIENTIFIC

LABORATORY NOTES

Electrochemical Cells

In this experiment we will prepare several different half-cells and connect them to find the voltages generated. We will use these values to construct a table of relative electrode potentials. Next we will change the concentration of one of the solutions to see how this affects the cell potential. Thirdly, we will measure the electrical potential of a cell containing silver and silver chloride. Using the measured potential and the Nernst equation, we will determine the solubility product of silver chloride. Lastly, a cell containing copper(II) and ammonia will be constructed. The potential and the Nernst equation will be used to calculate the formation constant of the tetraamminecopper(II) complex ion. The experiment uses a microscale technique.

An electrochemical cell results when an oxidation and a reduction reaction occur, and the electron transfer is made through an external wire. A half-cell can be prepared from almost any metal in contact with a solution of its ions. Since each element has its own electron configuration, each will develop a different electrical potential, and combinations of the different half-cells will result in different voltages.

The standard reduction potential is the voltage that a half-cell develops when it is combined with the hydrogen electrode, which is assigned a potential of zero volts. A chart of reductions listed in order of decreasing standard reduction potential shows the relative ease of reduction of each substance. The more positive the reduction potential, the easier the reduction will be. A spontaneous cell (a battery) can be constructed if one connects two half-cells internally using a salt bridge, and externally using a metallic connector. The reaction listed in the standard reduction potential chart which has the more positive voltage will occur as a reduction, and the reaction listed with the less positive voltage will reverse and occur as an oxidation reaction. The cell voltage can be found by combining the voltages in the table.

$$Cu^{2+}(aq) + 2\,e^- \rightarrow Cu(s) \qquad\qquad E° = 0.34 \text{ V}$$

$$Al^{3+}(aq) + 3\,e^- \rightarrow Al(s) \qquad\qquad E° = -1.66 \text{ V}$$

The reaction which has the more positive potential remains a reduction reaction. The reaction with the less positive (more negative) potential is reversed and becomes an oxidation. Its potential is now an oxidation potential:

$$Al(s) \rightarrow Al^{3+}(aq) + 3\,e^- \qquad\qquad E° = +1.66 \text{ V}$$

The reduction potential and the oxidation potential are combined to find the cell voltage:

$$E°_{cell} = E°_{reduction} + E°_{oxidation}$$

$$E°_{cell} = 0.34 \text{ V} + 1.66 \text{ V} = 2.00 \text{ V}$$

The table of standard potentials assumes that all ion concentrations are 1.0 M, gas pressures are 1 atm, and temperature is 25°C. Calculations of potentials at nonstandard concentrations can be made using the Nernst equation:

$$E = E° - \frac{R\,T}{n\,F}\,\ln Q$$

where E = a measured voltage, $E°$ = the standard voltage, R is the gas constant, 8.314 J/mol•K, n = the number of moles of electrons transferred as shown by the oxidation–reduction equation, and F is the Faraday, 9.65×10^4 C/mol. Q is the reaction quotient: the actual concentrations of products and reactants substituted into the equilibrium constant expression.

If we use base 10 or common logarithms the expression can be written:

$$E = E° - \frac{2.303\,R\,T}{nF}\,\log Q$$

If we substitute for the constants 2.303, R, and F, and use a temperature of 25°C (298K) the expression can be simplified to:

$$E = E° - \frac{0.0592}{n}\,\log Q$$

A measurement of the actual cell potential, E, can be used to calculate the value of Q which can then be used to find unknown concentrations of ions actually present in a solution.

In our experiment we will first construct a "standard" table of electrode potentials. However, we will assign a value of 0.00 volts to the electrode made from zinc metal in a 1.0 M solution of zinc ions. Our voltage values should correlate with those found in published tables, but they will differ by the value of $E°$ for the standard zinc electrode. One other difference is that published standard values are measured in solutions which have very small electrical resistance. The resistance of our cell will probably cause a lowering of measured values from the ideal values.

Chemicals

Copper(II) nitrate, $Cu(NO_3)_2$, 1.0 M

Iron(III) nitrate, $Fe(NO_3)_3$, 1.0 M

Lead(II) nitrate, $Pb(NO_3)_2$, 1.0 M

Magnesium nitrate, $Mg(NO_3)_2$, 1.0 M

Silver nitrate, $AgNO_3$, 1.0 M

Zinc nitrate, $Zn(NO_3)_2$, 1.0 M

Sodium chloride, NaCl, 1.0 M

Ammonia, NH_3, 6.0 M

Copper, Cu(s)

Iron, Fe(s)

Lead, Pb(s)

Magnesium, Mg(s)

Silver, Ag(s)

Zinc, Zn(s)

Potassium nitrate, KNO_3, 1.0 M

Vinegar

Equipment

24-well Microplate

Graduated cylinder, 10 mL

Wires and alligator clips

Test tubes, 13 × 150-mm

Beral pipets or droppers

Filter paper

Voltmeter

Beakers, 50-mL

Procedure

1. **Determine Reduction Potentials.**

   Prepare a test cell to measure the voltage of the copper and zinc half-cells. Put approximately 2 mL 1.0 M $Zn(NO_3)_2$ solution in one of the center wells of a 24-well plate. Put approximately 2 mL of 1.0 M $Cu(NO_3)_2$ in an adjacent well. Polish small strips of zinc and copper metal, and place the metal in the appropriate well containing the solution of the ions of that metal. Take a small strip of filter paper that has been soaked in KNO_3 solution, and drape it across the wells so that one end dips in the solution in each well. This will act as the salt bridge.

   Use a voltmeter to measure the potential difference between the two half-cells. Connect the meter so the voltage reading is positive. Use the most sensitive scale which is practical. Make note as to which electrode is the anode and which is the cathode. When the voltmeter reads a positive voltage, the electrode connected to the positive terminal is the cathode and is undergoing reduction, while oxidation is occurring at the electrode connected to the negative (or common) terminal, the anode.

   Prepare half-cells in other wells of the 24-well plates. First make a diagram of the order of the solutions in the wells so that you will not confuse the different solutions. Pour some 1.0 M solution of each of the ions below into different wells. Polish the metals with sandpaper or steel wool so that they are shiny, and insert them into the well which contains the ion of the same metal. Use fresh strips of filter paper soaked in 1.0 M potassium nitrate as salt bridges. The electrodes to be tested are:

$Ag \mid Ag^+$	$Mg \mid Mg^{2+}$
$Cu \mid Cu^{2+}$	$Pb \mid Pb^{2+}$
$Fe \mid Fe^{3+}$	$Zn \mid Zn^{2+}$

   The zinc electrode will be designated as the standard electrode. Measure the potential difference between the zinc electrode and each of the other electrodes. Record the data in your laboratory notebook in a chart similar to the one shown below.

   Voltage of Each Half-Cell versus the Zinc Electrode:

	Voltage	Anode	Cathode
Zn versus Ag			
Zn versus Cu			
Zn versus Fe			
Zn versus Mg			
Zn versus Pb			

Write reduction equations for each metal ion, arranging the equations in decreasing order of measured potential in an "E°" type of table. Include zinc in your table, using 0.00 volts as the potential of the $Zn \mid Zn^{2+}$ half-cell. Record the standard potentials using the hydrogen electrode as standard, and calculate the difference between the two values. Use a data table like the one shown below:

Reduction Equations for Each Ion Arranged in Decreasing Order of Potential:

Reduction equation	Electrode Potentials using Zinc as the Standard, E_{Zn}	Accepted Electrode Potentials using Hydrogen as Standard, $E°$	$E_{Zn} - E°$

2. **Measure Cell Potentials.**

Measure the potential difference between at least six combinations of the various electrodes. Use your table of electrode potentials to predict the voltage and which half-cell will be the anode and which the cathode. Compare the predicted and the measured potentials. Make a table in your laboratory notebook like the following in which you can record your data:

Predicted and Measured Cell Potentials:

Anode	Cathode	Equation for the cell reaction	Predicted Potential from Experimental Data	Measured Potential

3. **Change Ion Concentration.**

Dilute the 1.0 M $Cu(NO_3)_2$ so it is 0.0010 M. Count 18 drops of distilled water into a small test tube, and add 2 drops of the 1.0 M $Cu(NO_3)_2$ solution. Mix well by pouring back and forth from one test tube to another. This solution is now 0.10 M. Repeat this dilution process two more times, preparing a solution which is 0.0010 M. Pour some of this 0.0010 M $Cu(NO_3)_2$ solution into one of the wells in the well plate. Add a piece of polished copper wire and measure the voltage against the standard zinc electrode.

A representation of the cell is:

$$Zn(s) \mid Zn^{2+}(1.0 \, M) \parallel Cu^{2+}(0.0010 \, M) \mid Cu(s)$$

Record the data. Write a balanced net ionic equation for the reaction occurring in the cell. Use the Nernst equation to calculate what the expected voltage should be, and compare to the measured voltage.

4. Find the Solubility Product of AgCl.

Pour 10 mL of 1.0 M NaCl solution into a beaker. Add one drop of 1.0 M AgNO$_3$ to the NaCl solution, and stir well. Almost all of the silver ions will combine with chloride ions to precipitate AgCl. Since there is such a large excess of Cl$^-$, it can be assumed that the concentration of Cl$^-$ is still 1.0 M. The concentration of Ag$^+$ will be very small.

Pour some of the solution into one of the wells in the well plate and add a silver metal electrode. Measure the potential difference versus this half-cell and the zinc half-cell.

A representation of the cell is:

$$Zn(s) \mid Zn^{2+}(1.0 \, M) \parallel Ag^+(unknown \, M) \mid Ag(s)$$

Write a balanced net ionic equation for the reaction occurring in the cell. Use the Nernst equation to calculate the concentration of the Ag$^+$ ion. Calculate the value of the solubility product of AgCl. Compare the calculated value to a reported value.

5. Find the Formation Constant of Cu(NH$_3$)$_4^{2+}$.

Find the volume of one drop of 1.0 M Cu(NO$_3$)$_2$ solution by counting the number of drops in 1 mL. Put 10 mL of 6.0 M NH$_3$ in a beaker and add one drop of 1.0 M Cu(NO$_3$)$_2$ solution. Stir well. Pour some of the solution into one of the wells in the well plate and add a copper metal electrode. Measure the potential difference versus the zinc electrode. Write a balanced net ionic equation for the reaction occurring in the cell.

A representation of the cell is:

$$Zn(s) \mid Zn^{2+}(1.0 \, M) \parallel Cu^{2+}(unknown \, M) \mid Cu(s)$$

In the 6.0 M ammonia solution, almost all of the copper will combine with ammonia to form the complex ion Cu(NH$_3$)$_4^{2+}$. In this large excess of NH$_3$ we can assume that the ammonia concentration is still 6.0 M. The Cu(NH$_3$)$_4^{2+}$ concentration is calculated by assuming that all of the Cu^{2+} in solution is present as the complex ion. The uncomplexed Cu^{2+} concentration is calculated from the cell potential using the Nernst equation. Find the value of the formation constant, the equilibrium constant for the equation:

$$Cu^{2+}(aq) \, + \, 4 \, NH_3(aq) \rightleftarrows Cu(NH_3)_4^{2+}$$

Compare the calculated value to a value reported in the literature.

Disposal and Cleanup

Empty the solutions and solids into a beaker provided for them. Add excess solid magnesium and allow the solution to stand overnight. Filter off the solid metals. Dispose of the solutions according to the *Flinn Chemical & Biological Catalog/Reference Manual*, Flinn Suggested Disposal Method #26b, and the solids using Flinn Suggested Disposal Method #27d, or see the appendix of the teacher's manual.

Clean the well plate with detergent and cotton swabs.

Discussion

Answer the following questions in your laboratory notebook:

1. What is an electrode potential?

2. Did your ranking of reduction equations agree with that in a published chart of $E°$ values?

3. How should the values found using the zinc electrode as a standard compare with those in the $E°$ table that are based on the standard hydrogen electrode? Did they?

4. What factors can cause a difference between experimental and reported values?

5. What does a negative value for a standard potential indicate?

6. How did the change in concentration of the copper ions affect the cell potential? Did the calculated and measured values agree? Is this change in agreement (qualitatively) with that which would be predicted by LeChâtelier's Principle?

7. Explain how the AgCl solubility product was determined.

8. Explain how the formation constant for $Cu(NH_3)_4^{2+}$ was determined.

9. Comment on the agreement between measured and reported values for the equilibrium constants.

Electrochemical Cells

Preliminary Lab Assignment

Name_____ Date_____ Class_____

The following data were measured using a nickel electrode as the standard:

	Potential, volts
$Cu^{2+}(aq) + 2\,e^- \rightarrow Cu(s)$	+0.62
$Ni^{2+}(aq) + 2\,e^- \rightarrow Ni(s)$	+0.00
$Fe^{2+}(aq) + 2\,e^- \rightarrow Fe(s)$	−0.15
$Al^{3+}(aq) + 3\,e^- \rightarrow Al(s)$	−1.38

1. Which ion is most easily reduced?

2. Which metal is most easily oxidized?

3. The copper and aluminum electrodes are connected in a battery.

    a) Which is the anode?

    b) Which is oxidized?

    c) What will the battery voltage be?

    d) Write a balanced net ionic equation for the reaction that takes place.

4. A solution is prepared in which a slight amount of Fe^{2+} is added to a much larger amount of solution in which the $[OH^-]$ is 1.0×10^{-2} M. Some $Fe(OH)_2$ precipitates. The value of K_{sp} of $Fe(OH)_2 = 8.0 \times 10^{-10}$.

    a) Assuming that the hydroxide ion concentration is 1.0×10^{-2} M, calculate the concentration of Fe^{2+} in the solution.

    b) A battery is prepared in which the above solution with an iron wire dipping into it is one half-cell. The other half-cell is the standard nickel electrode. Write the balanced net ionic equation for the cell reaction.

    c) Use the Nernst equation to calculate the potential of the above cell.

Qualitative Analysis of Cations

Analysis of Solutions Containing the Ions
Ag^+, Pb^{2+}, Hg_2^{2+}, Fe^{3+}, Cu^{2+}, Mn^{2+}, Zn^{2+}, Al^{3+}, Co^{2+} and Bi^{3+}

Qualitative analysis is an analytical procedure in which the question "what is present?" is answered. In a systematic qualitative analysis scheme, each substance present is separated from the other substances. Then a confirmatory test is used to prove that the isolated substance is the expected one.

In this experiment you will analyze a solution that can contain any combination of ten different cations. First of all, you will prepare a solution that is "known" to contain all of the ions, and you will analyze this solution to learn the techniques for the analysis. Then you will analyze an "unknown" solution to determine which ions are present and which are absent.

This experiment is carried out on a semi-micro scale. Very small quantities of reagents are used. Cleanliness and a great deal of care are necessary to obtain good results.

As you go through the steps of the analysis, keep a copy of the flow chart available for reference. The flow chart appears at the end of the experimental directions. It will help you to see the "total picture" of where you are and where you are heading. Read the directions carefully, and read the sections which give the notes or chemical theory for each step. Don't just follow directions "cook book" style, but make an effort to understand the chemical principles behind the procedures.

General Techniques for Qualitative Analysis

Keep Good Records

It is necessary to keep good records so that you will not get confused and forget what solutions are in which test tubes. Number your test tubes with pencil or permanent ink so the numbers do not come off in the hot water bath. You should be able to write on the white spots on the test tubes.

Maintain a current record of your work. Don't trust your results to your memory. In your laboratory notebook, set up a table with columns marked:

			Known Solution		Unknown Solution	
Step	Procedure		Results	Conclusion	Results	Conclusion
1	Add HCl to known solution in TT1. Centrifuge. Pour the colored solution into TT2		White ppt forms Other ions present in solution in TT2.	Ag^+, Pb^{2+}, and/or Hg_2^{2+} present		

Note: TT is short for test tube. Fill out the columns for the "Known Solutions" first. Then, when analyzing the "Unknown Solutions," fill out the last two columns.

Be Orderly

Arrange your chemical reagents in a way so that you can easily find the solutions you need. You might put acids together, bases next, etc.

Avoid Contamination

Tap water is often a source of contaminating ions. Wash all glassware and rinse with distilled water.

A stirring rod is constantly used to mix solutions, and it also must be rinsed with distilled water so that it does not contaminate subsequent solutions. An easy way to do this is to fill a 400-mL beaker about 2/3 full of distilled water, and keep your stirring rods in this beaker. The small amount of contaminants present in this volume of water should cause no problem. Replace the distilled water if it appears to need it.

Droppers should also be rinsed twice with distilled water after they are used. Get in the habit of rinsing them immediately after use.

When you use the chemical reagents, do not turn the droppers upside down. This causes the reagent to go into the rubber dropper top, which may dissolve the dropper top and contaminate your solution.

Measuring Solutions

Generally, you should estimate the volume of solutions added. It is not necessary to use a graduated cylinder to measure solution volumes. You might wish to calibrate a test tube in milliliter to give yourself an idea of what volume a milliliter actually is. You may also want to count the number of drops in a milliliter, determine the volume that a dropper can deliver, or use a calibrated Beral pipet.

Heating Solutions

Frequently it will be necessary to heat a solution to speed up a reaction. Do NOT heat small test tubes over Bunsen burner flames. A sudden steam bubble will cause the solution to shoot out of the test tube. Instead, heat test tubes in a boiling water bath. A good idea is to set up this bath when you begin work in the lab.

Stirring Solutions

Each time a reagent is added to a test tube, the solution needs to be stirred. It is important to mix the solutions at the top and the bottom of the test tube. A stirring rod that is flattened at the bottom can be used as a plunger to effectively mix solutions in the narrow test tubes.

Separating Solids from Solutions

Centrifuge solutions so that the solid is packed at the bottom of the test tube. Don't forget that you need to counterbalance test tubes in the centrifuge with similar test tubes holding equivalent volumes of liquid. Let the centrifuge spin for about 30 seconds. Usually the supernatant liquid (the liquid above the precipitate) can be poured off of the precipitate. Sometimes precipitates tend to float on the surface of the solution. If this is the case, use a Pasteur (capillary) pipet to draw off the supernatant liquid. It is better to leave a little liquid over the precipitate than to transfer some of the precipitate.

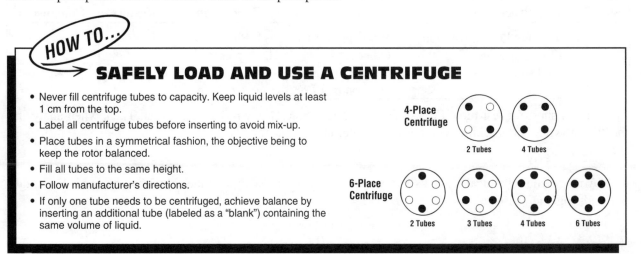

HOW TO...

SAFELY LOAD AND USE A CENTRIFUGE

- Never fill centrifuge tubes to capacity. Keep liquid levels at least 1 cm from the top.
- Label all centrifuge tubes before inserting to avoid mix-up.
- Place tubes in a symmetrical fashion, the objective being to keep the rotor balanced.
- Fill all tubes to the same height.
- Follow manufacturer's directions.
- If only one tube needs to be centrifuged, achieve balance by inserting an additional tube (labeled as a "blank") containing the same volume of liquid.

4-Place Centrifuge — 2 Tubes — 4 Tubes

6-Place Centrifuge — 2 Tubes — 3 Tubes — 4 Tubes — 6 Tubes

Washing Precipitates

It is almost always necessary to wash precipitates to free them from ions which might cause confusion in later steps. To do this, add 1 or 2 mL of distilled water to the precipitate, stir, centrifuge, and discard the wash water. Sometimes the directions will tell you to include a specific reagent in the wash water.

Checking the pH

To check the pH of a solution, put a piece of litmus paper or pH paper on a clean glass plate or watch glass. Dip the stirring rod into the solution in the test tube, and touch the stirring rod to the paper. Do NOT dip the test paper into the test tube. This may cause some of the indicator dye to dissolve in the solution, and the indicator color may confuse subsequent tests.

Storing Solutions

If you wish to keep a solution until the next laboratory period, be sure to stopper the test tube with a cork stopper. If a precipitate is present, put a few drops of distilled water on it before stoppering the test tube. Be sure to include in your record a list of what substances are present in each test tube. Don't trust your memory!

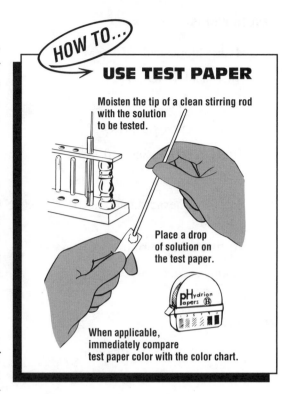

HOW TO...

USE TEST PAPER

Moisten the tip of a clean stirring rod with the solution to be tested.

Place a drop of solution on the test paper.

When applicable, immediately compare test paper color with the color chart.

Disposal of Solutions

Many of the ions to be tested are poisons, and solutions containing these substances should not be washed down the sink. This is especially true for the ions of heavy metals such as silver, lead and mercury. Use a few drops of water to suspend precipitates containing these ions in solution, and empty them into a container marked for this purpose. Your teacher will dispose of the precipitates and solutions safely. Refer to the *Flinn Chemical & Biological Catalog/Reference Manual*, Flinn Suggested Disposal Methods #27f and #26b, or see the appendix of the teacher's manual.

Chemicals

Solutions of cations

Silver nitrate, $AgNO_3$, 0.2 M

Mercury(I) nitrate, $Hg_2(NO_3)_2$, 0.2 M

Copper(II) nitrate, $Cu(NO_3)_2$, 0.2 M

Zinc nitrate, $Zn(NO_3)_2$, 0.2 M

Cobalt(II) nitrate, $Co(NO_3)_2$, 0.2 M

Lead nitrate, $Pb(NO_3)_2$, 0.5 M

Iron(III) nitrate, $Fe(NO_3)_3$, 0.2 M

Manganese(II) nitrate, $Mn(NO_3)_2$, 0.2 M

Aluminum nitrate, $Al(NO_3)_3$, 0.2 M

Bismuth(III) nitrate, $Bi(NO_3)_3$, 0.2 M

Test reagents

Hydrochloric acid, HCl, 6 M

Nitric acid, HNO_3, 6 M

Ammonia, NH_3, 6 M

Hydrogen peroxide, H_2O_2, 3%

Tin(II) chloride, $SnCl_2$, 0.1 M

Sodium bismuthate, $NaBiO_3(s)$

Potassium hexacyanoferrate(II), $K_4[Fe(CN)_6]$, 0.1 M

Sulfuric acid, H_2SO_4, 6 M

Acetic acid, $HC_2H_3O_2$, 6 M

Sodium hydroxide, NaOH, 6 M

Potassium thiocyanate, KSCN, 0.1 M

Aluminon solution, 0.1%

Potassium nitrite, $KNO_2(s)$

To neutralize spills

Baking soda, $NaHCO_3(s)$

Vinegar, $HC_2H_3O_2$

Equipment

Test tubes, 6, 13 × 100-mm

Wire test tube holder

Beaker, 400-mL for rinsing stirring rods

Spatula

Capillary pipet

Beral pipet, graduated (optional)

Centrifuge

Test tube rack

Beaker, 250-mL for hot water bath

Stirring rods

Ring stand, ring, wire gauze, burner

Corks to fit test tubes

Litmus paper or pH paper

Procedure

Safety Alert

Most of the acids and bases used are very concentrated and can cause chemical burns if spilled. Handle them with care. If you get acid or base on yourself, wash it off with lots of water. Small spills (a few drops) can be cleaned up with paper towels. Larger acid spills can be neutralized with baking soda, $NaHCO_3$, and then safely cleaned up. Neutralize base spills with a vinegar solution (dilute acetic acid). Some of the solutions are poisonous. Wash your hands when you are finished.

Solutions containing silver ions cause stains which do not appear for several hours. If you think you spilled any of the solution containing silver ions on yourself, wash off with soap and water.

Wear Chemical Splash Goggles and a Chemical-Resistant Apron.

Preparation of a Solution for Analysis

Prepare a known solution by combining three drops of each ion to be tested. The total solution volume will be about 2 mL.

To analyze an unknown solution, use about 1.5 mL of the solution that your teacher will give you.

Note that the following directions are written for a "known" solution that contains all of the cations. An "unknown" solution will probably not form all of the products described in this procedure. You should make note of any differences as you analyze your "unknown" solution.

In the directions that follow, a description of the physical properties and the chemistry of the substances appears in boxed frames:

> *Aqueous solutions of Ag^+, Pb^{2+}, Hg_2^{2+}, Zn^{2+}, Al^{3+}, and Bi^{3+}, are all colorless. Fe^{3+} has a yellow color, Cu^{2+} is blue, Mn^{2+} is an extremely pale pink, and Co^{2+} is a deeper pink in aqueous solution.*

1. **Separation of the Silver Group (Ag^+, Pb^{2+}, and Hg_2^{2+}) from Manganese, Cobalt, Iron, Bismuth, Copper, Aluminum and Zinc Ions.**

> *Most chloride salts are soluble; however, Ag^+, Pb^{2+}, and Hg_2^{2+} ions form insoluble white chlorides. These three ions can be separated from the other ions present in this qualitative analysis scheme by precipitating them as chlorides. All of the other ions will stay in solution.*
>
> $Ag^+(aq) + Cl^-(aq) \rightarrow AgCl(s)$
>
> $Pb^{2+}(aq) + 2Cl^-(aq) \rightarrow PbCl_2(s)$
>
> $Hg_2^{2+}(aq) + 2Cl^-(aq) \rightarrow Hg_2Cl_2(s)$

Add 8 drops of 6 M HCl to the solution to be analyzed. Stir. A white precipitate indicates that one or more of the ions Ag^+, Pb^{2+}, and Hg_2^{2+} is present. Centrifuge the solution and test to be sure that precipitation is complete by adding one more drop of 6 M HCl. No additional precipitate should form. If more precipitate does form, continue adding 6 M HCl until precipitation is complete. Centrifuge and decant (pour off) the clear liquid into a second test tube for step 5. Alternatively, you can use a Pasteur (capillary) or Beral pipet to draw off the supernatant liquid to transfer it to another test tube.

Wash the precipitate by adding 1 mL distilled water and stirring. Centrifuge and discard the wash water.

2. **Separation and Confirmation of Lead.**

> *Lead chloride is considerably more soluble in hot water than cold water. Silver chloride and mercury(I) chloride are not very soluble at all in hot water.*
>
> $PbCl_2(s) \rightarrow Pb^{2+}(aq) + 2Cl^-(aq)$
>
> *The confirmatory test for lead is the formation of the white precipitate of $PbSO_4$ when H_2SO_4 is added.*
>
> $Pb^{2+}(aq) + SO_4^{2-}(aq) \rightarrow PbSO_4(s)$

Add 1 mL of distilled water to the precipitate of AgCl, $PbCl_2$, and Hg_2Cl_2 and heat in a boiling water bath for about 3 minutes with occasional stirring. Centrifuge the hot solution, and quickly pour off the supernatant liquid.

To the clear liquid, add 5 drops of 6 M H_2SO_4. A white precipitate of $PbSO_4$ confirms the presence of lead. If lead ions are found to be present, check to be sure that all of the lead is removed from the AgCl and Hg_2Cl_2 precipitates by repeating the process of adding distilled water, heating, centrifuging and pouring off the clear liquid until the addition of H_2SO_4 to the liquid no longer forms a precipitate. Dispose of the lead sulfate by placing it in the container provided.

3. Separation of Silver and Mercury; Confirmation of Mercury.

When 6 M NH_3 is added to AgCl, the Ag^+ forms a colorless complex ion and goes into solution:

$AgCl(s) + 2NH_3(aq) \rightleftarrows Ag(NH_3)_2{}^+(aq) + Cl^-(aq)$

The addition of the 6 M NH_3 to the Hg_2Cl_2 causes the mercury(I) ion to undergo a disproportionation reaction. In disproportionation, the same substance is both oxidized and reduced. In this reaction, half of the mercury(I) ions is reduced to elemental mercury, $Hg^0(l)$, while the other half of the ions is oxidized to mercury(II), Hg^{2+}. The Hg^{2+} forms a white precipitate of $HgNH_2Cl$, mercury(II) amido chloride. The metallic Hg^0 appears black in its finely divided form. The mixture of the two substances appears dark gray. The appearance of the dark gray solid is confirmation of the presence of the mercury(I) ion.

$Hg_2Cl_2(s) + 2\,NH_3(aq) \rightarrow Hg(l) + HgNH_2Cl(s) + NH_4{}^+(aq) + Cl^-(aq)$

To the precipitate from step 2, which is AgCl and Hg_2Cl_2, add 1 mL 6 M NH_3. The appearance of the dark gray precipitate confirms the presence of mercury (I). Stir, centrifuge, and transfer the solution to another test tube for step 4. Dispose of the mercury compounds in the container provided.

4. Confirmation of Silver.

Addition of hydrochloric acid to the $Ag(NH_3)_2{}^+$ complex ion breaks apart the ion. The NH_3 combines with H^+ to form $NH_4{}^+$, and the Ag^+ recombines with the Cl^- ion to precipitate as white AgCl.

$Ag(NH_3)_2{}^+(aq) + Cl^-(aq) + 2H^+(aq) \rightarrow AgCl(s) + 2NH_4{}^+(aq)$

Add 15 drops of 6 M HCl to the solution. The solution will smoke and the reaction between the strong acid and the base will give off heat whether or not silver is present. The test tube may get very warm. Stir and test with pH indicator paper or litmus paper to be sure the solution is acidic. If it is not acidic, add more HCl. The reappearance of the white AgCl precipitate in the acidic solution confirms the presence of silver. Dispose of the silver compound in the container provided.

5. Separation of Manganese, Cobalt, Iron, Bismuth and Copper from Aluminum and Zinc.

In a basic solution, the amphoteric zinc and aluminum will form colorless complex ions and remain in solution, while the hydroxides of all the other ions will precipitate. Adding hydrogen peroxide to the basic solution will oxidize Mn^{2+} to Mn^{4+}, and will oxidize Co^{2+} to Co^{3+}. Manganese will precipitate as black MnO_2, and the other ions will precipitate as hydroxides: rust colored $Fe(OH)_3$, blue $Cu(OH)_2$, white $Bi(OH)_3$, and brown $Co(OH)_3$. The reactions are as follows:

$$Mn^{2+}(aq) + 2OH^-(aq) \rightarrow Mn(OH)_2(s)$$

$$Mn(OH)_2(s) + H_2O_2(aq) \rightarrow MnO_2(s) + H_2O(l)$$

$$Co^{2+}(aq) + 2OH^-(aq) \rightarrow Co(OH)_2(s)$$

$$2Co(OH)_2(s) + H_2O_2(aq) \rightarrow 2Co(OH)_3(s)$$

$$Fe^{3+}(aq) + 3OH^-(aq) \rightarrow Fe(OH)_3(s)$$

$$Bi^{3+}(aq) + 3OH^-(aq) \rightarrow Bi(OH)_3(s)$$

$$Cu^{2+}(aq) + 2OH^-(aq) \rightarrow Cu(OH)_2(s)$$

$$Al^{3+}(aq) + 4OH^-(aq) \rightarrow Al(OH)_4^-(aq)$$

$$Zn^{2+}(aq) + 4OH^-(aq) \rightarrow Zn(OH)_4^{2-}(aq)$$

To the solution saved from step 1, add 10 drops of 3% hydrogen peroxide, H_2O_2. With stirring, add 6 M sodium hydroxide, NaOH, until the solution is basic and then add 3 more drops. Stir and place the test tube in a hot water bath for 3 minutes. You should see the formation of a precipitate which will be the solids listed above. Check the colors of the compounds. If all ions are present, it will be a dark-colored precipitate. Centrifuge the solution, and separate the clear solution from the solid. Save the clear solution, which may contain $Zn(OH)_4^{2-}$ and $Al(OH)_4^-$ ions for step 13. Wash the precipitate with a mixture of 10 drops of 6 M NaOH and 10 drops of water. Centrifuge and discard the wash water.

6. Separate Manganese and Cobalt Ions from Iron, Bismuth and Copper Ions.

Manganese(IV) oxide, MnO_2, does not dissolve well in acid or base unless it is oxidized or reduced. Cobalt(III) hydroxide, $Co(OH)_3$, will also not dissolve readily in acid unless a reducing agent such as H_2O_2 is present. The other hydroxides that are present will readily dissolve in acid solution.

$$Fe(OH)_3(s) + 3H^+(aq) \rightarrow Fe^{3+}(aq) + 3H_2O(l)$$

$$Cu(OH)_2(s) + 2H^+(aq) \rightarrow Cu^{2+}(aq) + 2H_2O(l)$$

$$Bi(OH)_3(s) + 3H^+(aq) \rightarrow Bi^{3+}(aq) + 3H_2O(l)$$

Add 5 drops of water to the precipitate from step 5. Then add 6 M H_2SO_4 dropwise until the solution is acidic when tested with litmus paper (about 6 drops). Centrifuge and separate the precipitate which may be dark brown to black MnO_2 and $Co(OH)_3$ from the supernatant liquid which will contain the yellow Fe^{3+}, blue Cu^{2+}, and colorless Bi^{3+} ions. Save the solution for step 10. Wash the precipitate with water, centrifuge, and discard the wash water.

7. Manganese and Cobalt Ions.

Manganese(IV) oxide and cobalt(III) hydroxide will dissolve in acid solution when a reducing agent is present. Notice that in acid solution H_2O_2 can act as a reducing agent. In step 3, however, H_2O_2 in basic solution functioned as an oxidizing agent.

$$MnO_2(s) + H_2O_2(aq) + 2H^+(aq) \rightarrow Mn^{2+}(aq) + O_2(g) + 2H_2O(l)$$

$$2Co(OH)_3(s) + H_2O_2(aq) + 4H^+(aq) \rightarrow 2Co^{2+}(aq) + O_2(g) + 6H_2O(l)$$

To the precipitate from step 6 add 1 mL of water and 1 mL of 6 M H_2SO_4. Add 1 mL of 3% H_2O_2 and heat in a boiling water bath with stirring. The precipitate should dissolve quickly leaving very little residue. When the precipitate has dissolved, pour half of the solution into a second test tube.

8. Confirmation of Manganese.

In dilute HNO_3, the bismuthate ion, BiO_3^- will oxidize Mn^{2+} to the purple permanganate ion, MnO_4^-. The presence of this purple ion in solution is the confirmatory test for manganese. Co^{2+} does not interfere.

$$2Mn^{2+}(aq) + 14H^+(aq) + 5BiO_3^-(aq) \rightarrow 2MnO_4^-(aq) + 5Bi^{3+}(aq) + 7H_2O(l)$$

To one-half of the solution from step 7 add 1 mL of 6 M HNO_3, and add a spatula of solid sodium bismuthate, $NaBiO_3$. Some excess solid sodium bismuthate should remain. Add more if needed. Stir and centrifuge to determine the color of the supernatant liquid. The purple color of the MnO_4^- ion in solution confirms the presence of manganese. Dispose of the manganese in the container provided.

9. Confirmation of Cobalt.

When potassium nitrite is added to acidic solutions containing the Co^{2+} ion, a yellow precipitate of potassium hexanitritocobaltate(III) forms, $K_3[Co(NO_2)_6]$. This compound is sometimes called potassium cobaltinitrite, and is one of the few insoluble potassium compounds.

$$Co^{2+}(aq) + 2H^+(aq) + 7NO_2^-(aq) + 3K^+(aq) \rightarrow NO(g) + H_2O(l) + K_3[Co(NO_2)_6](s)$$

The colorless NO gas that forms quickly reacts with oxygen in the air to form the red-brown gas NO_2.

PERFORM THIS STEP IN THE FUME HOOD OR UNDER A FUNNEL ATTACHED TO AN ASPIRATOR. To the remaining half of the solution from step 7, slowly add a spatula of KNO_2 solid. The formation of a yellow precipitate of $K_3[Co(NO_2)_6]$ confirms the presence of cobalt. This step must be carried out in the fume hood because the NO and NO_2 gases which form are toxic. While you are still at the hood, fill the test tube with water and dispose of the contents in the container provided in the hood.

10. Separation of Iron and Bismuth from Copper; Confirmation of Copper.

Aqueous ammonia added to a solution in which Cu^{2+} is present, will cause the deep blue tetraammine copper(II) complex ion to form. The presence of this deep blue color confirms the presence of copper. At the same time, the basic ammonia solution will precipitate the hydroxides of iron and bismuth.

$Cu^{2+}(aq) + 4NH_3(aq) \rightleftarrows Cu(NH_3)_4^{2+}(aq)$

$Fe^{3+}(aq) + 3OH^-(aq) \rightarrow Fe(OH)_3(s)$

$Bi^{3+}(aq) + 3NH_3(aq) + 3H_2O(l) \rightarrow Bi(OH)_3(s) + 3 NH_4^+(aq)$

An additional and very sensitive confirmatory test for copper is to precipitate the red-brown copper(II) hexacyanoferrate(II) [also called copper(II) ferrocyanide], $Cu_2[Fe(CN)_6](s)$, from a Cu^{2+} solution.

$2Cu^{2+}(aq) + Fe(CN)_6^{4-}(aq) \rightarrow Cu_2[Fe(CN)_6](s)$

To the solution from step 6 add 6 M aqueous NH_3 until the solution is basic to litmus, and then add 1 mL extra. Centrifuge and separate the supernatant liquid from the precipitate. Save the precipitate for step 11. The presence of the blue $Cu(NH_3)_4^{2+}$ ion is the confirmatory test for copper.

If you wish an additional confirmatory test, to the solution containing the $Cu(NH_3)_4^{2+}$ add 6 M $HC_2H_3O_2$ until the blue color fades and the solution becomes acidic. Then add 2 drops of 0.1 M $K_4[Fe(CN)_6]$. A red-brown precipitate of $Cu_2[Fe(CN)_6]$ reconfirms the presence of copper.

Dispose of the copper solution in the container provided.

11. Confirmation of Iron.

Both bismuth(III) hydroxide and iron(III) hydroxide will dissolve in sulfuric acid. Addition of the thiocyanate ion, SCN^-, forms a deep wine-red colored complex ion with iron that is a very sensitive test for the presence of iron. The bismuth ions will not interfere with this test.

$Bi(OH)_3(s) + 3H^+(aq) \rightarrow Bi^{3+}(aq) + 3 H_2O(l)$

$Fe(OH)_3(s) + 3 H^+(aq) \rightarrow Fe^{3+}(aq) + 3 H_2O(l)$

$Fe^{3+}(aq) + SCN^-(aq) \rightleftarrows FeSCN^{2+}(aq)$

Wash the precipitate of bismuth and iron hydroxides from step 10. Then add 6 M H_2SO_4 dropwise until the precipitate dissolves. Pour half of this solution into a second test tube to save for step 12.

To one-half of the solution add 5 drops of 0.1 M KSCN solution. The deep red $FeSCN^{2+}$ ion confirms the presence of iron. Dispose of the iron solution in the container provided.

12. Confirmation of Bismuth.

> When a solution which contains a bismuth salt and chloride ions is added to a large volume of water, the bismuth will precipitate as the white compound BiOCl. This is a confirmatory test for bismuth. Iron ions do not interfere.
>
> $$Bi^{3+}(aq) + Cl^-(aq) + H_2O(l) \rightleftarrows BiOCl(s) + 2H^+(aq)$$
>
> An additional confirmatory test for bismuth is to add the reducing agent tin(II) chloride, $SnCl_2$, to a basic solution containing $Bi(OH)_3$. The Sn^{2+} will reduce the Bi^{3+} to neutral, black, metallic bismuth. Iron ions do not interfere.
>
> $$2Bi(OH)_3(s) + 3Sn(OH)_4^{2-}(aq) \rightarrow 2Bi(s) + 3Sn(OH)_6^{2-}(aq)$$

Add 2 drops of 6 M HCl to the remaining solution from step 11. Stir. Then add 2 or 3 drops of this mixture to 300 mL of tap water. The presence of a white cloudiness due to BiOCl confirms the presence of bismuth.

If you wish additional confirmation, add 6 M NaOH to the remaining solution until a white precipitate of $Bi(OH)_3$ forms, and add 10 additional drops of NaOH. Next add 5 drops of 0.1 M $SnCl_2$ solution. The formation of the black bismuth precipitate reconfirms the presence of bismuth.

Dispose of the bismuth solution in the container provided.

13. Separation of Zinc and Aluminum.

> The colorless zinc and aluminum ions can be separated from one another because the aluminum forms an insoluble hydroxide in ammonia solution, while the zinc forms a soluble complex ion with ammonia. The insoluble aluminum hydroxide is a translucent, gelatinous precipitate that is difficult to see.
>
> $$Zn(OH)_4^{2-}(aq) + 4 H^+(aq) \rightarrow Zn^{2+}(aq) + 4 H_2O(l)$$
>
> $$Zn^{2+}(aq) + 4NH_3(aq) \rightarrow Zn(NH_3)_4^{2+}(aq)$$
>
> $$Al(OH)_4^-(aq) + 4H^+(aq) \rightarrow Al^{3+}(aq) + 4H_2O(l)$$
>
> $$Al^{3+}(aq) + 3NH_3(aq) + 3H_2O(l) \rightarrow Al(OH)_3(s) + 3NH_4^+(aq)$$

To the colorless solution from step 5 add about 10 drops 6 M HNO_3. Test to see if the solution is acidic. Continue to add HNO_3 until the solution is acidic. Then add 6 M NH_3 dropwise until the solution is basic to litmus. Add an additional 3 drops of the 6 M NH_3. Stir the solution. A gelatinous precipitate of $Al(OH)_3$ will be present. It is difficult to see the precipitate. Centrifuge, and carefully separate the supernatant liquid from the precipitate.

14. Confirmation of Aluminum.

> The confirmation of aluminum is carried out by dissolving the $Al(OH)_3$ precipitate in acid, adding a red dye called aluminon to the solution, and then reprecipitating the $Al(OH)_3$. The red dye will be adsorbed in the gelatinous precipitate making the precipitate easier to see. This red gelatinous precipitate is called a "lake".
>
> $$Al(OH)_3(s) + 3H^+(aq) \rightarrow Al^{3+}(aq) + 3H_2O(l)$$
>
> $$Al^{3+}(aq) + 3NH_3(aq) + 3H_2O(l) \rightarrow Al(OH)_3(s) + 3 NH_4^+(aq)$$

Dissolve the precipitate from step 13 in 6 M HCl. Add 3 drops of aluminon solution, and then add 6 M NH_3 until the solution is basic to litmus. The red aluminon should be adsorbed by the gelatinous $Al(OH)_3$. Centrifuge so that it is easier to see if the aluminon is adsorbed by the precipitate rather than coloring the solution red. The red precipitate confirms the presence of aluminum. Dispose of the aluminum precipitate and solution in the container provided.

15. Confirmation of Zinc.

> *The confirmatory test for zinc is the formation of a precipitate of potassium zinc hexacyanoferrate(II), $K_2Zn_3[Fe(CN)_6]_2$. This precipitate is nearly white if pure, but if a trace of iron is present, it may appear light green or blue-green in color.*
>
> $$Zn(NH_3)_4{}^{2+}(aq) + 4H^+(aq) \rightarrow Zn^{2+}(aq) + 4NH_4{}^+(aq)$$
>
> $$3Zn^{2+}(aq) + 2K^+(aq) + 2Fe(CN)_6{}^{4-}(aq) \rightarrow K_2Zn_3[Fe(CN)_6]_2(s)$$

Make the solution from step 13 slightly acidic using 6 M HCl added dropwise. Add 3 drops of 0.1 M $K_4[Fe(CN)_6]$ and stir. Centrifuge to see the confirmatory precipitate of $K_2Zn_3[Fe(CN)_6]_2$ which will be white to light green or blue green in color. Dispose of the zinc precipitate and solution in the container provided.

Disposal

Your teacher will add solid zinc to the waste collected from this experiment and allow it to stand for several days. Then the solids will be filtered from the liquid. The solids and liquid will be disposed of according to the *Flinn Chemical & Biological Catalog/Reference Manual*, Flinn Suggested Disposal Methods #26b and #27f, or see the appendix of the teacher's manual.

Discussion

Your laboratory report should contain all of your data from the analysis of the known solution as well as your unknown solution. State clearly which ions were shown to be present and which ions were proven absent.

In your report also include answers to the following questions:

1. What is the precipitating reagent for the silver group (Ag^+, $Hg_2{}^{2+}$, and Pb^{2+})? Would a solution of NaCl work as well? Why or why not?

2. In the analysis scheme, Ag^+ is precipitated as AgCl, the precipitate is dissolved, and then AgCl is precipitated again in the confirmatory step. Explain the chemistry of each of these steps by showing a balanced equation for each.

3. When NH_3 is added to solid Hg_2Cl_2, some of the mercury ions are oxidized and some are reduced. A reaction where the same substance is both oxidized and reduced is called a disproportionation reaction. Write equations for each of these half-reactions.

4. H_2O_2 can act either as an oxidizing agent or a reducing agent depending on the acidity of the solution. Write half-reactions for H_2O_2 acting as an oxidizing agent and a reducing agent.

5. In this qualitative analysis scheme a number of precipitates form and then dissolve when complex ions are formed. Write three equations which show a precipitate dissolving as a complex ion forms.

6. In separating Mn^{2+} from other ions, it is oxidized, reduced, and then oxidized. Write the equations for each of the steps, and state the oxidation number of manganese in each product.

7. When Fe^{3+} and Cu^{2+} react with NH_3 solution they form two different types of products. One is a precipitate and one a complex ion in solution. Write equations for these two reactions. NH_3 solution is used in the same manner to separate two other ions later in the analytical scheme. Write equations for these two reactions.

8. Al^{3+} and Zn^{2+} are said to be amphoteric because their hydroxides dissolve in both acid and base. Write equations to show aluminum hydroxide and zinc hydroxide dissolving in excess hydroxide ion as in step 5, and then in excess hydrogen ion as in step 13.

References

Slowinski, E. J.; Masterton, W. L.; Saunders College Publishing: *Qualitative Analysis and the Properties of Ions in Aqueous Solution*; New York 1990.

Metz, C.; Castellion, M. E.; Saunders College Publishing: *Chemistry—Inorganic Qualitative Analysis in the Laboratory*, New York 1989.

Qualitative Analysis of Cations

Flow Chart

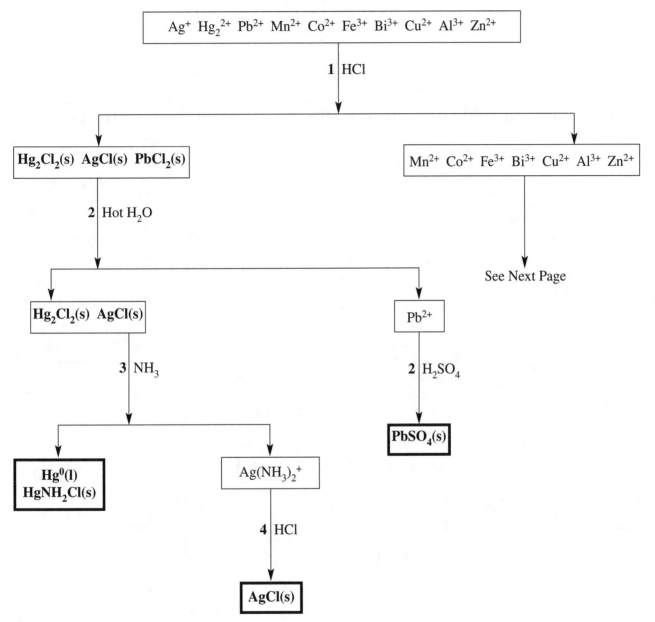

Note

Each branch in the flow chart indicates a separation. Solids are listed to the left; solutions are on the right.

Boldface type indicates that a solid or liquid is present.

Ions in regular weight type are all present in aqueous solution.

Substances shown in heavy rule boxes are confirmatory substances.

Flow Chart, continued

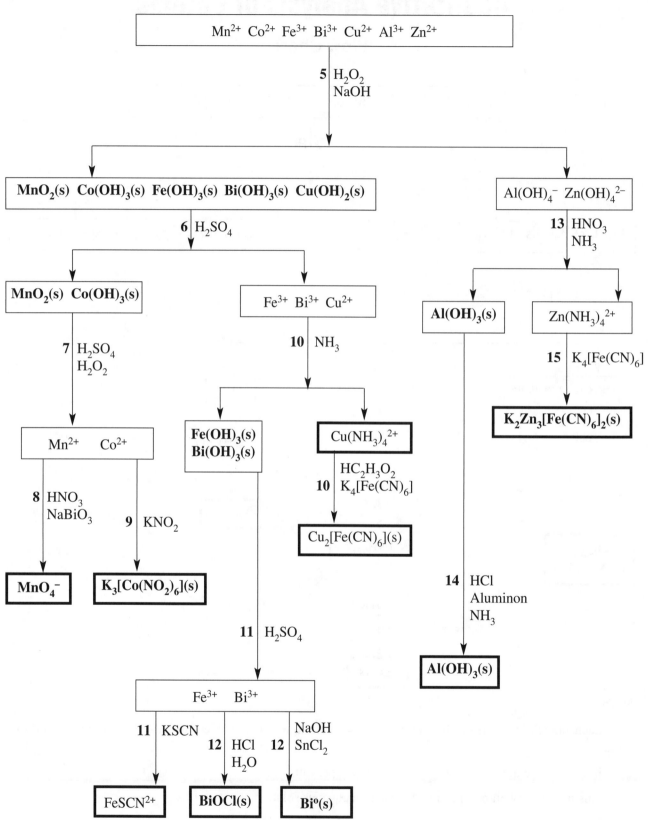

$$Mn^{2+} \quad Co^{2+} \quad Fe^{3+} \quad Bi^{3+} \quad Cu^{2+} \quad Al^{3+} \quad Zn^{2+}$$

5 | H_2O_2
NaOH

$$MnO_2(s) \quad Co(OH)_3(s) \quad Fe(OH)_3(s) \quad Bi(OH)_3(s) \quad Cu(OH)_2(s)$$

$$Al(OH)_4^- \quad Zn(OH)_4^{2-}$$

6 | H_2SO_4

13 | HNO_3
NH_3

$$MnO_2(s) \quad Co(OH)_3(s)$$

$$Fe^{3+} \quad Bi^{3+} \quad Cu^{2+}$$

$$Al(OH)_3(s)$$

$$Zn(NH_3)_4^{2+}$$

7 | H_2SO_4
H_2O_2

10 | NH_3

15 | $K_4[Fe(CN)_6]$

$$Mn^{2+} \quad Co^{2+}$$

$$Fe(OH)_3(s)$$
$$Bi(OH)_3(s)$$

$$Cu(NH_3)_4^{2+}$$

$$K_2Zn_3[Fe(CN)_6]_2(s)$$

$HC_2H_3O_2$
10 | $K_4[Fe(CN)_6]$

8 | HNO_3
$NaBiO_3$

9 | KNO_2

$$Cu_2[Fe(CN)_6](s)$$

$$MnO_4^-$$

$$K_3[Co(NO_2)_6](s)$$

14 | HCl
Aluminon
NH_3

11 | H_2SO_4

$$Al(OH)_3(s)$$

$$Fe^{3+} \quad Bi^{3+}$$

11 | KSCN

12 | HCl
H_2O

12 | NaOH
$SnCl_2$

$$FeSCN^{2+}$$

$$BiOCl(s)$$

$$Bi^o(s)$$

Qualitative Analysis of Cations

Preliminary Lab Assignment

Name_____ Date_____ Class_____

Use the flow charts at the end of the experimental procedure to answer the following questions. In each question, a test is carried out to determine the presence or absence of several ions. Only those listed may be present. State if the tests indicate if each ion is present, absent, or undetermined.

1. Test for Ag^+, Hg_2^{2+}, and Pb^{2+}

   Some 6 M HCl is added to a solution which may contain the three ions. A white precipitate forms. All of the precipitate dissolves in hot water.

   Ions present: _____ Ions absent: _____ Ions undetermined: _____

2. Test for Ag^+ and Hg_2^{2+}

   A white precipitate which may be AgCl and/or Hg_2Cl_2 is treated with 6 M NH_3. A black precipitate forms.

   Ions present: _____ Ions absent: _____ Ions undetermined: _____

3. Test for Mn^{2+}, Co^{2+}, Fe^{3+}, Bi^{3+}, and Zn^{2+}

   A colorless solution is known to contain one or more of the above ions. Some 3% H_2O_2 and NaOH are added and the solution heated for several minutes. A white precipitate forms.

   Ions present: _____ Ions absent: _____ Ions undetermined: _____

4. Test for Cu^{2+}, Al^{3+}, and Zn^{2+}

   Addition of 6 M NH_3 to a solution known to contain one or more of the above ions causes the formation of a deep blue colored solution containing a gelatinous precipitate.

   Ions present: _____ Ions absent: _____ Ions undetermined: _____

5. Test for Mn^{2+}, Co^{2+}, Fe^{3+}, Bi^{3+}, and Cu^{2+}

   Some 3% H_2O_2 and 6 M NaOH is added to a pale blue solution. A dark precipitate forms which totally dissolves in 6 M H_2SO_4. Addition of 6 M NH_3 to the solution until it is basic results in a deep blue solution containing a dark precipitate. The dark precipitate completely dissolves in H_2SO_4.

   Ions present: _____ Ions absent: _____ Ions undetermined: _____

6. Test for Mn^{2+} and Co^{2+}

   A solution which may contain these ions is acidified with 6 M HNO_3 and then solid sodium bismuthate, $NaBiO_3$, is added until some excess solid remains. No purple color forms.

   Ions present: _____ Ions absent: _____ Ions undetermined: _____

7. Test for Hg_2^{2+}, Co^{2+}, and Al^{3+}

   Some 6 M HCl is added to the colorless solution. No precipitate forms. Next, some 3% H_2O_2 and 6 M NaOH are added until the solution is basic, and it is then heated. No precipitate forms. The solution is acidified with 6 M HNO_3 and then made basic with 6 M NH_3. No precipitate forms.

   Ions present: _____ Ions absent: _____ Ions undetermined: _____

8. Test for Ag^+, Fe^{3+}, Bi^{3+}, and Zn^{2+}

   Some 6 M HCl is added to the colorless solution. A white precipitate forms and is removed. The solution is then made basic with 6 M NaOH. No precipitate forms.

   Ions present: _____ Ions absent: _____ Ions undetermined: _____

Only one of each of the following pairs of reactants undergoes a reaction. Complete and balance the equation for the reaction which occurs.

9. $Co(OH)_2(s)$ + NaOH(aq) $\rightarrow$

   $Al(OH)_3(s)$ + NaOH(aq) $\rightarrow$

10. AgCl(s) + NH_3(aq) $\rightarrow$

    $Bi(OH)_3(s)$ + NH_3(aq) $\rightarrow$

11. $Al(OH)_3(s)$ + NH_3(aq) $\rightarrow$

    $Cu(OH)_2(s)$ + NH_3(aq) $\rightarrow$

12. Fe^{3+}(aq) + SCN^-(aq) $\rightarrow$

    Bi^{3+}(aq) + SCN^-(aq) $\rightarrow$

13. $Co(OH)_3(s)$ + H^+(aq) $\rightarrow$

    $Zn(OH)_2(s)$ + H^+(aq) $\rightarrow$

Qualitative Analysis of Anions

Analysis of Solutions Containing the Ions
Cl^-, Br^-, I^-, SO_4^{2-}, CO_3^{2-}, and NO_3^-

This experiment continues the qualitative analysis begun in Experiment 19. Here we analyze solutions to determine the presence of anions. The same techniques that were used for the cation analysis must be used for the anions. If you have not carried out Experiment 19, read the introductory section before starting this experiment. The major difference between cation and anion analysis is that in anion analysis, a series of separations of the ions from one another is usually not the most efficient way to determine their presence. Instead, only some separations will be made, and the initial test solution will be used to test many of the ions. Refer to the flow chart at the end of the experimental directions as you proceed.

First you will prepare and analyze a "known" solution which contains all six of the anions. Then you will analyze an "unknown" solution using the same techniques, to determine the presence or absence of each anion.

As in Experiment 19, a description of the physical properties and the chemistry of the substances appears in boxed frames.

Chemicals

Solutions of Anions

Sodium chloride, NaCl, 0.2 M

Potassium iodide, KI, 0.2 M

Sodium carbonate, Na_2CO_3, 0.2 M

Sodium bromide, NaBr, 0.2 M

Sodium sulfate, Na_2SO_4, 0.2 M

Sodium nitrate, $NaNO_3$, 0.2 M

Test Reagents

Silver nitrate, $AgNO_3$, 0.1 M

Nitric acid, HNO_3, 6 M

Mineral oil

Barium hydroxide, $Ba(OH)_2$, saturated

Acetic acid, $HC_2H_3O_2$, 6 M

Iron(III) nitrate, $Fe(NO_3)_3$ 0.1 M in nitric acid, HNO_3, 0.6 M

Ammonia, NH_3, 6 M

Potassium permanganate, $KMnO_4$, 0.1 M

Sodium hydroxide, NaOH, 6 M

Barium chloride, $BaCl_2$, 0.1 M

Aluminum(s), granules

To neutralize spills

Baking soda, $NaHCO_3$(s)

Vinegar, $HC_2H_3O_2$

Equipment

Test tubes, 6, 13 × 100-mm	Test tube rack
Wire test tube holder	Beaker, 250-mL for hot water bath
Beaker, 400-mL for rinsing stirring rods	Stirring rods
Ring stand, ring, wire gauze, burner	Corks to fit test tubes
Beral pipet, graduated (optional) or capillary dropper	pH paper or litmus paper
Centrifuge	Cotton

Procedure

Safety Alert

Most of the acids and bases used are very concentrated and can cause chemical burns if spilled. Handle them with care. Wash acid or base spills off of yourself with lots of water. Small spills (a few drops) can be cleaned up with paper towels. Larger acid spills can be neutralized with baking soda, $NaHCO_3$, and then safely cleaned up. Neutralize base spills with a vinegar solution (dilute acetic acid). Some of the compounds are poisonous. Wash your hands when finished.

Solutions containing silver ions and potassium permanganate solutions cause stains which do not appear immediately. If you suspect that you spilled any of these solutions on yourself, wash off with soap and water.

Wear Chemical Splash Goggles and a Chemical-Resistant Apron.

Preparation of a Solution for Analysis.

Prepare a known solution containing 1 mL of each of the anions to be tested. This solution will be referred to as the original test solution.

Your teacher will provide you with an "unknown" solution to be analyzed.

Note that the following directions are written for a "known" solution that contains all of the anions. An "unknown" solution will probably not form all of the products described in this procedure. You should make note of any differences as you analyze your "unknown" solution.

Aqueous solutions of all of the anions to be tested are colorless. The positive ion associated with each of the anions will be either sodium or potassium ion.

1. **Separation of the Halides (Cl⁻, Br⁻, I⁻); Confirmation of Chloride.**

> *The halides all form insoluble silver compounds. Silver chloride is a white solid, silver bromide is pale cream-colored solid, and the solid silver iodide is light yellow in color.*
>
> $$Cl^-(aq) + Ag^+(aq) \rightarrow AgCl(s)$$
>
> $$Br^-(aq) + Ag^+(aq) \rightarrow AgBr(s)$$
>
> $$I^-(aq) + Ag^+(aq) \rightarrow AgI(s)$$
>
> *Silver chloride is the only silver halide that dissolves in 6 M ammonia, NH_3, forming the colorless ion $Ag(NH_3)_2^+$. If nitric acid, HNO_3, is added to a solution containing this ion, the ammonia in the complex reacts with hydrogen ions to form ammonium ions, and the silver recombines with the chloride ions which are still present in solution.*
>
> $$AgCl(s) + 2\ NH_3(aq) \rightarrow Ag(NH_3)_2^+(aq) + Cl^-(aq)$$
>
> $$Ag(NH_3)_2^+(aq) + Cl^-(aq) + 2\ H^+(aq) \rightarrow AgCl(s) + 2\ NH_4^+(aq)$$

Place 10 drops of the original test solution (or unknown solution) in a test tube. Test to see if the solution is acidic. If it is not, add 6 M acetic acid, $HC_2H_3O_2$, dropwise with stirring until the solution is acidic. Add 10 drops of 0.1 M silver nitrate, $AgNO_3$. A precipitate of AgCl, AgBr, and AgI will form. Centrifuge and pour off the supernatant liquid. Wash the solid with 0.5 mL distilled water, centrifuge and discard the wash water.

Add 0.5 mL 6 M ammonia, NH_3, to the precipitate. Stir to dissolve any AgCl. Centrifuge, and pour the supernatant liquid into another test tube to test for chloride ion. Discard the precipitate of AgBr and AgI in a container provided for disposal of waste solutions.

Add 1 mL 6 M nitric acid, HNO_3, to the solution containing the dissolved silver chloride. The solution will get hot and smoke from the reaction with the excess ammonia whether or not silver chloride is present. Test with litmus or pH paper to see if the solution is acidic. If it is not, add more HNO_3 until the solution is acidic. The appearance of the white precipitate of AgCl in the acidic solution confirms the presence of chloride.

2. **Separation and Confirmation of Bromide and Iodide.**

> *In acid solution, iron(III) ion, Fe^{3+}, is a weak oxidizing agent capable of oxidizing the easily oxidized iodide ion to iodine. Bromide and other ions present will not interfere. The nonpolar iodine will preferentially dissolve in nonpolar mineral oil, where it can be identified by its pink to violet color.*
>
> $$2\ I^-(aq) + 2\ Fe^{3+}(aq) \rightarrow I_2(aq) + 2\ Fe^{2+}$$
>
> *$KMnO_4$ is a stronger oxidizing agent than the iron(III) nitrate and will oxidize bromide, Br^-, to bromine, Br_2. Other ions present will not interfere. The nonpolar bromine can be extracted into nonpolar mineral oil where it can be identified by its characteristic yellow to brown color.*
>
> $$10\ Br^-(aq) + 2\ MnO_4^-(aq) + 16\ H^+(aq) \rightarrow 5\ Br_2(aq) + 2\ Mn^{2+}(aq) + 8\ H_2O(l)$$

Place 10 drops of the original test solution (or unknown solution) in a test tube. Add 6 M HNO_3 dropwise with stirring until the solution is acidic. Add 1 mL 0.1 M $Fe(NO_3)_3$ in 0.6 M HNO_3 solution and stir. Then add 1 mL of mineral oil, stopper the test tube with a cork stopper and shake for 30 seconds. The presence of a pale pink to purple color in the mineral oil layer (the top layer) due to dissolved iodine confirms the presence of I^- in the original solution.

Draw the mineral oil layer off the solution with a capillary dropper and discard in the container provided for waste solutions. Repeat the extraction with fresh mineral oil until all the iodine is removed. Discard the mineral oil layer. Add 0.1 M $KMnO_4$ solution to the aqueous layer dropwise with stirring until the solution remains pink. Again add 1 mL mineral oil, cork and shake the test tube for 30 seconds. The presence of a yellow to brown color in the mineral oil layer due to dissolved bromine confirms the presence of Br^- in the original solution. Discard the solution in the container provided.

3. Confirmation of Carbonate.

> *In acid solution, carbonate forms carbon dioxide gas and water. The carbon dioxide may be seen as a slight effervescence. Carbon dioxide is less soluble in hot water than cold water.*
>
> *When carbon dioxide gas is passed through a saturated solution of barium hydroxide, it readily forms a precipitate of white barium carbonate.*
>
> $CO_3^{2-}(aq) + 2\ H^+(aq) \rightarrow CO_2(g) + H_2O(l)$
>
> $CO_2(g)\ + Ba^{2+}(aq) + 2\ OH^-(aq) \rightarrow BaCO_3(s) + H_2O(l)$

If any bubbles were formed when acid was added to the original solution, carbonate is probably present and carbon dioxide is being formed. A confirmation of the presence of carbonate involves reacting evolving carbon dioxide with barium hydroxide to form white, insoluble barium carbonate.

Place 2 mL of clear, saturated $Ba(OH)_2$ solution in a test tube to be available for the test with carbon dioxide. Place 1 mL of the original test solution (or unknown solution) in a different test tube. Acidify this solution by adding 0.5 mL of 6 M HNO_3. Place the tube in a hot water bath and observe to see if any gas bubbles form. Take a dry Beral pipet and squeeze the bulb closed. Place the tip of the pipet close to (but not touching) the surface of the liquid in the test tube and slowly release the bulb to draw escaping carbon dioxide into the pipet. Put the pipet into the barium hydroxide solution, and slowly squeeze the bulb, causing the gas in the pipet to bubble through the barium hydroxide solution. This procedure may be repeated. The formation of a cloudy white precipitate of barium carbonate confirms the presence of carbonate ion in the original solution.

4. Confirmation of Sulfate.

> *The test for sulfate is the formation of white, insoluble barium sulfate. This solid is insoluble even in acidic solution.*
>
> $SO_4^{2-}(aq) + Ba^{2+}(aq) \rightarrow BaSO_4(s)$

Place 0.5 mL of the original test solution (or unknown solution) in a test tube. Add 6 M acetic acid, $HC_2H_3O_2$, dropwise until the solution is acidic. Then add 0.5 mL 0.1 M $BaCl_2$ solution. The formation of a white precipitate of $BaSO_4$ confirms the presence of sulfate.

5. Confirmation of Nitrate.

> *The test for nitrate involves the reduction of nitrate ions in basic solution to ammonia, NH_3, using solid aluminum as the reducing agent. When the solution is heated, ammonia gas is liberated. The evolving ammonia gas will turn litmus paper from pink to blue.*
>
> $$3\,NO_3^-(aq) + 8\,Al(s) + 5\,OH^-(aq) + 18\,H_2O(l) \rightarrow 3\,NH_3(g) + 8\,Al(OH)_4^-(aq)$$

Place 1 mL of the original test solution (or unknown solution) in a test tube. Add 6 M NaOH dropwise until the solution is basic, and then add 6 drops in excess. Use a Beral pipet to transfer the solution to the bottom of a dry test tube without getting the walls of the test tube wet with solution. Add the tip of a spatula of aluminum granules. Place a small cotton wad loosely about halfway down the test tube, but not touching the solution. This is to prevent spattering of the solution onto the litmus paper. Hang a piece of moist red litmus paper (or pH paper) in the tube so that the bottom of the paper is close to (but not touching) the cotton. Now warm the solution in a hot water bath until it starts bubbling strongly. Be sure that the solution and the cotton do not touch the litmus paper. Allow the solution to cool. A slow color change (within 3 to 5 minutes) of the litmus from pink to blue, starting at the bottom and spreading to the top, indicates the evolution of ammonia and confirms the presence of nitrate in the original solution.

Disposal

Your teacher will provide a waste container for the solutions used in this experiment. The teacher will add solid zinc and some sodium sulfate to the waste collected. The substances may be safely disposed of using the method in the *Flinn Chemical & Biological Catalog/Reference Manual*, Flinn Suggested Disposal Method #11 (procedure B), or see the appendix of the teacher's manual.

Discussion

In your laboratory discussion include answers to the following questions:

1. The confirmatory test for chloride ion with silver ion is the same chemical reaction used to confirm silver in the cation analysis scheme. Explain what the reaction is and how the initial precipitate is dissolved and reprecipitated. Use equations in your explanation.

2. The procedure for chloride analysis makes use of the fact that AgCl can be dissolved in ammonia, but neither AgBr nor AgI will dissolve in ammonia. Look up the solubility products of AgCl, AgBr and AgI and show how their relative solubilities agree with this fact.

3. Refer to a table of standard reduction potentials to find the values for the reduction of Cl_2, Br_2, I_2, MnO_4^-, and Fe^{3+}. List the reduction reactions according to the E° values. From the listing determine which of the halides can be oxidized by Fe^{3+} and which can be oxidized by acidic MnO_4^-.

4. Explain why it is necessary to test for iodide by oxidation with Fe^{3+} before the test for bromide by oxidation with MnO_4^- is done.

5. Write separate oxidation and reduction half-reactions for the procedure used in the test for nitrate ions.

6. In the nitrate test, why must care be taken to keep the moist litmus from coming in contact with the cotton or the solution?

7. In step 4, Ba^{2+} is added to the solution containing all six of the anions and precipitates $BaSO_4$, but not $BaCO_3$. However, in step 3, the precipitation of $BaCO_3$ is the confirmatory test for carbonate ion. Why doesn't $BaCO_3$ precipitate in step 4 but does in step 3?

Qualitative Analysis of Anions

Flow Chart

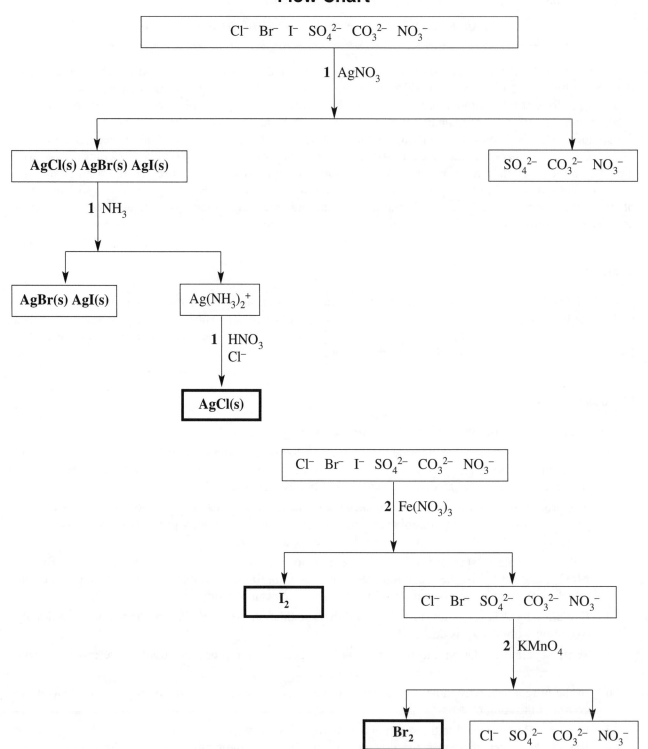

Flow Chart, continued

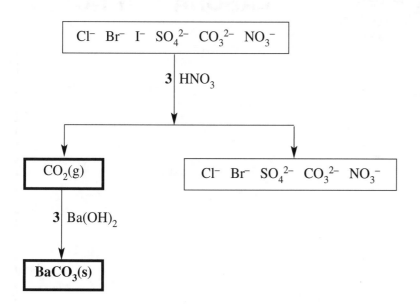

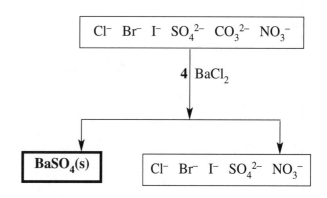

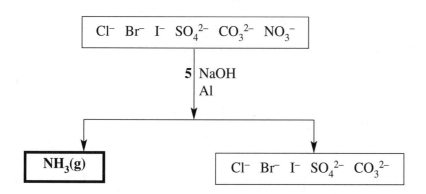

FLINN SCIENTIFIC

Qualitative Analysis of Anions

Preliminary Lab Assignment

Name_____ Date_____ Class_____

Use the flow chart at the end of the experimental directions to answer the following questions. In each question a test is carried out to determine the presence or absence of several ions. Only those ions listed may be present. State if the tests indicate if each of the ions is present, absent or undetermined.

1. Test for CO_3^{2-} and I^-

    Some 6 M HCl is added to the solution which may contain the above ions. Formation of bubbles is noted as the solution is heated.

    Ions present: _____ Ions absent: _____ Ions undetermined: _____

2. Test for Cl^-, Br^- and I^-

    Some $AgC_2H_3O_2$ solution is added to the test mixture. A white precipitate forms. The precipitate totally dissolves in 6 M NH_3.

    Ions present: _____ Ions absent: _____ Ions undetermined: _____

3. Test for Cl^-, Br^- and I^-

    The test solution is acidified and $KMnO_4$ is added until the solution remains pink. Some mineral oil is added and the mixture is shaken. After allowing the layers to separate, the mineral oil layer is purple.

    Ions present: _____ Ions absent: _____ Ions undetermined: _____

4. Test for Cl^-, Br^-, I^-, SO_4^{2-}, CO_3^{2-}, and NO_3^-

    Addition of $AgNO_3$ causes no precipitate to form. Addition of $BaCl_2$ also causes no precipitate to form.

    Ions present: _____ Ions absent: _____ Ions undetermined: _____

Only one of each of the following pairs of reactants undergoes a reaction. Complete and balance the equation for the reaction which occurs.

5. $NaI(aq) \ + \ BaCl_2(aq) \ \rightarrow$

    $Na_2SO_4(aq) \ + \ BaCl_2(aq) \ \rightarrow$

6. $NO_3^-(aq) \ + \ OH^-(aq) \ + \ Al(s) \ \rightarrow$

    $CO_3^{2-}(aq) \ + \ OH^-(aq) \ + \ Al(s) \ \rightarrow$

7. $K^+(aq) \ + \ Br^-(aq) \ \rightarrow$

    $Ag^+(aq) \ + \ Br^-(aq) \ \rightarrow$

FLINN SCIENTIFIC

Liquid Chromatography

In this experiment we will use liquid chromatography to separate the substances that are present in grape flavored Kool-Aid®. First, the dyes FD&C Blue #1 and Red #40 will be separated. The other components of Kool-Aid®, the flavorings and citric acid, will be separated in a second experiment.

Chromatography is an important analytical tool that is used to separate the components of a mixture. Liquid chromatography is one type of chromatography that is enormously useful in research and in industry. High performance liquid chromatography (HPLC) has become an almost indispensable tool for scientists. There are many kinds of chromatography, but all have some elements in common. First, there is a stationary support medium which attracts the components of the mixture. This medium may be polar, attracting polar components of the mixture, or nonpolar, attracting the nonpolar components. In liquid chromatography, this support is a column packed with a fine, granular solid. The mixture to be seperated is placed in the column and clings to the solid. The second necessary component is a solvent which washes along the column. This solvent has a different polarity than the solid. The components of the mixture may be more strongly attracted to the solvent or to the stationary support, depending on their polarity. As the solvent washes through the column, the components of the mixture spend some time adsorbed on the stationary support and some time dissolved in the moving solvent. The substances that are more soluble in the solvent travel more quickly through the column, and emerge early. Those substances that are more strongly attracted to the stationary support move slowly, and emerge later.

A C18 Sep-Pak® cartridge is the column that will be used in this experiment. This column is packed with a silica solid which has a C_{18} hydrocarbon bonded to it, so it is very nonpolar.

A third component of chromatography is that a means of injecting the sample into the column is required. We will use a disposable hypodermic syringe. Fourth, a pump is needed to force the solvent through the column. We will use a syringe or plastic squeeze bottle. Next, a detector is required to tell when the components emerge from the column. Since we will be separating colored dyes, we can use our eyes to see the dyes as they emerge from the column. The recording of the experiment will be done manually with pen and a laboratory notebook.

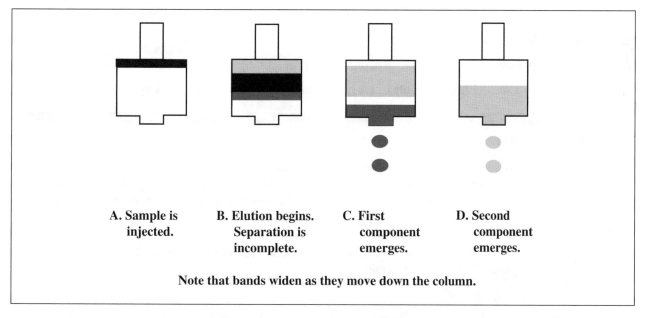

| A. Sample is injected. | B. Elution begins. Separation is incomplete. | C. First component emerges. | D. Second component emerges. |

Note that bands widen as they move down the column.

Figure 1. Components of Mixture Moving through Liquid Chromatography Column

When a mixture is injected into the liquid chromatography column and washed through it, several processes occur. Refer to Figure 1. The more polar components of the mixture are attracted more strongly to the solvent, so they will move more quickly through the column with the solvent. The less polar components will move more slowly, as they spend more time adsorbed to the column medium. Ideally, the components should emerge at different times. A measure of the degree of separation that is achieved is called the resolution of the system. A second process that occurs which works against resolution is that as the band of each component moves down the column, the band widens due to diffusion. As bands widen they overlap each other more easily and prevent clean separation or resolution of the components.

Chemicals

Isopropanol, C_3H_7OH, 70% or 91%, colorless, unscented

Grape Kool-Aid®, or other grape drink, unsweetened

Equipment

Sep-Pak® C18 cartridge

Graduated cylinders, 10-mL and 25-mL

Beakers, 4, 50-mL or 10-mL

Beakers, 4, 100-mL

Syringe, 1 mL or 2 mL with male Luer® tip

Syringe, 10-mL with male Luer® tip,
    or 50-mL or 100-mL dropper bottles with plastic tips,
    or 100-mL or 250-mL wash bottles

Procedure

Safety Alert

Isopropyl alcohol is flammable. Keep it away from flames.

Wear Chemical Splash Goggles and a Chemical-Resistant Apron.

Isocratic separation

In an isocratic separation, the solvent composition and flow rate are held constant throughout the experiment. The solvent composition is chosen to be able to elute both of the dyes in the grape drink at different rates. In an isocratic separation, the resolution, selectivity and efficiency of the separation can be calculated.

1. **Prepare Kool-Aid.**

   Prepare the grape Kool-Aid® as directed on the package, but omit the sugar. To prepare less than a whole package, use 0.5 g/250 mL water.

2. **Prepare the isopropanol eluant.**

   Prepare 18% (v/v) isopropanol in water to be used as the mobile phase. Combine 13 mL of 70% isopropanol with 37 mL distilled water (or 10 mL 91% isopropanol with 40 mL distilled water).

3. Pretreat the C18 Sep-Pak® cartridge.

To help eliminate remixing of closely eluting bands in the cartridge, cut off the exit tube of the cartridge (the shorter end) at the point where it meets the body of the cartridge. Pre-wet the cartridge by pumping about 10 mL of undiluted (70% isopropanol) through the cartridge.

If you are using a syringe, fill it with 10 mL of the undiluted isopropanol. Attach the tip to the long end of the Sep-Pak® cartridge, and pump the isopropanol through the syringe at a rate of 5–10 mL per minute. Collect the eluted alcohol in a 10 mL graduated cylinder to monitor the flow rate. If you are using a plastic bottle with a pointed dropper top or a wash bottle, attach the top of the filled bottle firmly to the cartridge, and slowly pump the isopropanol through the cartridge.

Next, wash the cartridge with 10 mL of distilled water at the same flow rate.

4. Inject the sample.

Use a small (1- or 2-mL) syringe to slowly inject 1 mL of the Kool-Aid sample onto the column. Discard the column effluent (the portion that washed out as you injected the sample).

5. Elute the sample.

Use a 10-mL syringe or a plastic dropper bottle to slowly elute the dyes. Fill the syringe or dropper bottle with the 18% isopropanol eluant, and pump at a steady rate of 5–10 mL per minute. Collect the column effluent in a 10-mL graduated cylinder. Record the volume of effluent collected as the first and last of the colored drops of each of the dyes emerge. If there is not a perfect separation between the blue- and red-colored bands, record data for the beginning and end of the intermediate purple band. The center of the purple band will serve as the end of the first band and beginning of the last.

6. Regenerate the cartridge and repeat the measurements.

Repeat the measurements two more times. Show all your data, and use the average values to make the calculations which are described below. Between injections, wash the column with 10 mL of distilled water at the same flow rate of 5–10 mL per minute. If colored material builds up on the column, repeat the pretreatment procedure.

7. Calculate the resolution, selectivity, and efficiency.

Determine the following values. Show how each calculation is carried out and record your data in a table like the one shown below. The shaded sections do not need to be filled in.

V_R is retention volume. The retention volumes for the dyes in the experiment are the volumes corresponding to the centers of the red and blue bands.

W is the band width, or the volume in mL of each dye as it emerges from the column.

V_{Ravg} is the total volume eluted at the center of the band of each of the dyes.

L is the column length. The cartridges in this experiment are 1.25 cm long.

The column radius is r. These cartridges have a radius of 0.5 cm.

V_M is mobile phase volume. This represents about 50% of the total empty column volume and can be estimated as $V_M = 0.5 \pi r^2 L$. The value of V_M will be in cm³ (mL) if r and L are measured in centimeters.

k' is the capacity factor. This is a unitless measure of the retention for each of the dyes, and can be calculated as $k' = (V_R - V_M) / V_M$. The optimum range for k' is between 1 and 10.

α is the selectivity or separation factor. It is the ratio of the separation of the k' values: $\alpha = k'_2 / k'_1$ where k'_2 is the larger k' value. For example, a value for α of 1.1 indicates that the column shows a 10% greater rententivity for the component that elutes second. Generally, a mobile phase is chosen which gives a value for α between 2 and 10.

N represents the number of theoretical plates in the column. This can be considered as the number of times a solute is exchanged back and forth between the stationary and the mobile phase. The calculation is based on the dye which is eluted last. Generally, columns with a larger value for N are more efficient. In the small cartridges used, N should have a value between 20 and 200.

R is the resolution. This represents the major goal of the experiment, the measure of how well the two components are separated by the column. $R = (V_{R1} - V_{R2}) / \frac{1}{2}(W_1 + W_2)$. The numerator is the volume between bands. This is related to the selectivity. The denominator represents the average band width, which is proportional to the efficiency of the column. As resolution increases above a value of 1, there is much greater total separation of the dyes.

Data Table

	Red Dye	**Blue Dye**	**Experimental System**
V_R (start)			
V_R (end)			
$W = V_R$ (end) $- V_R$ (start)			
$V_{Ravg} = V_R$ (start) $+ \frac{1}{2} W$			
L			
r			
$V_M = 0.5 \, \pi \, r^2 \, L$			
$k' = (V_{Ravg} - V_M) / V_M$			
$\alpha = k'_2 / k'_1$			
$N = 16 \, (V_R/W)^2$			
$R = (V_{R1} - V_{R2}) / \frac{1}{2} (W_1 + W_2)$			

Step Gradient Separation

In this type of procedure, the composition of the eluting liquid is changed. Since the column is nonpolar, first a very polar solvent, water, will be used. Then its composition will be changed to less polar by adding more isopropanol. With this procedure we will be able to separate the citric acid and flavoring oils as well as the dyes.

8. **Prepare the isopropanol eluants.**

   Prepare the following concentrations of isopropanol in water by mixing the suggested amounts:

   5% isopropanol in water: Mix 3.5 mL 70% isopropanol and 46.5 mL distilled water (or 2.8 mL 91% isopropanol and 47.2 mL distilled water).

   28% isopropanol in water: Mix 20.0 mL 70% isopropanol and 30.0 mL distilled water (or 15.5 mL 91% isopropanol and 34.5 mL distilled water).

9. Pretreat the cartridge.

Follow the same procedure as in step 3.

10. Inject the sample and elute the components.

Inject 1 mL of the grape drink. Elute the polar components of the mixture (citric acid and any sugar present) by passing 5 mL of water through the column. Collect the effluent in a small beaker. Next, elute the red dye by passing 5 to 10 mL of 6% isopropanol through the column. Note that large amounts of the 6% isopropanol can be used without eluting the blue dye. Collect this effluent in a second beaker. Thirdly, use the 28% isopropanol to elute the blue dye. Collect it in a third beaker. Lastly, use 8 mL of 70% isopropanol to elute the polar flavor oils and other nonpolar additives. Collect this fraction in a fourth beaker.

11. Evaporate the solvents and examine the components.

Allow the four beakers of solution to evaporate by leaving them in the fume hood until the next laboratory period. Observe and describe the contents of each of the beakers.

Disposal

Solutions can be safely flushed down the sink. The cartridges can be used again.

Discussion

In your laboratory report include answers to the following questions:

1. What is meant by polarity of molecules? What causes differences in polarity?

2. In discussing solubility, the rule "like dissolves like" is frequently used. What does this mean?

3. Draw the structural formula of isopropanol. Explain how it differs in polarity from water.

4. For good separation of the dyes, the resolution should be greater than one. What was the value you calculated? Did the two dyes overlap as they emerged from the column, or was the separation a good one?

5. In the step gradient separation, four separate fractions were collected. How were these related to the polarities of the column and of the eluting solvent?

References

Bidlingmeyer, B. A.; Warren Jr., F. V. "An Inexpensive Experiment for the Introduction of High Performance Liquid Chromatography" *J. Chem. Educ.* **1984**, *61*, 716–720.

Institute for Chemical Education, *Fun With Chemistry*; Vol. 1, Sarquis, Mickey and Sarquis, Gerry, Ed.; University of Wisconsin—Madison, 1991, 77–82.

Liquid Chromatography

Preliminary Lab Assignment

Name_____ Date_____ Class_____

1. What is the process of chromatography used for?

2. In chromatography, components of a mixture spend some time adsorbed on a stationary phase and some time dissolved in a mobile phase. Explain how the components can be separated with these two phases.

3. In the liquid chromatography column used in this experiment, the solid has a C18 hydrocarbon bonded to it. Would a C18 hydrocarbon be a polar or a nonpolar substance? Explain.

4. The Kool-Aid® that is to be separated in this experiment consists of citric acid, calcium phosphate, salt, maltodextrin, artificial flavor, ascorbic acid, FD&C Red #40 and FD&C Blue #1 dyes. Group these as very polar, moderately polar, or nonpolar.

5. Suggest a different mixture for which liquid chromatography might be a useful separation tool.

Preparation of Esters

An ester is a chemical compound that is formed when an organic acid reacts with an alcohol. Esters frequently have distinctive odors, and are found in the flavorings of many fruits and plants. The reaction between an organic acid and an alcohol is shown in Figure 1.

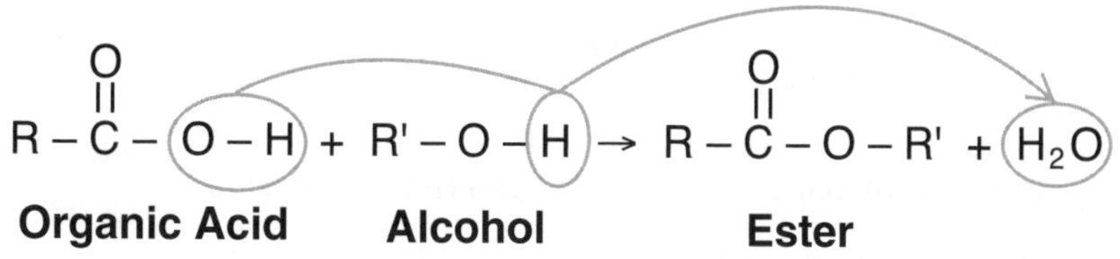

Figure 1. The Reaction Between An Organic Acid and Alcohol to Form an Ester and Water

In the diagram, R and R′ represent organic groups such as hydrocarbons. The –OH group from the acid combines with the –H from the alcohol producing water molecules. The R′–O– group from the alcohol then attaches to the carbon on the acid forming the ester. The reaction is catalyzed by adding some concentrated sulfuric acid, H_2SO_4. Concentrated sulfuric acid is a strong dehydrating agent, and helps the reaction by removing the water molecules as they are formed.

If acetic acid and methanol are reacted, the reaction shown in Figure 2 occurs. The product is called methyl acetate. The systematic name for acetic acid is ethanoic acid, and the product is also known as methyl ethanoate.

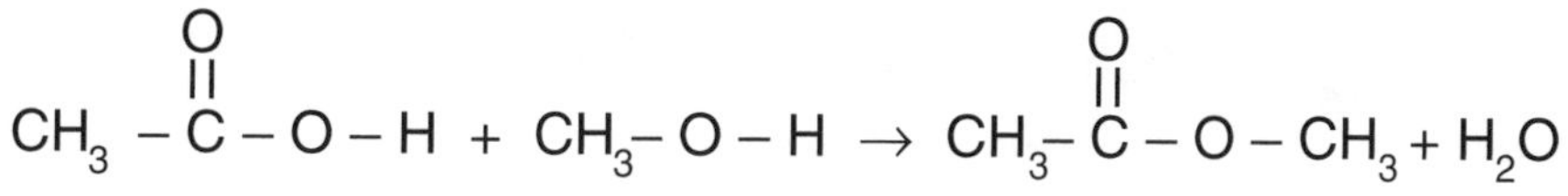

Figure 2. The Reaction between Acetic Acid (Ethanoic Acid) and Methanol

In this experiment we will prepare small quantities of several esters. The esters will be identified by their distinctive odors. Then we will prepare a larger quantity of the ester ethyl acetate (ethyl ethanoate) and purify it by distillation.

Chemicals

Part 1

Various combinations of acids and alcohols will be used which may contain the following:

Organic acids: Formic acid (methanoic acid)

                    Acetic acid (ethanoic acid)

                    Propionic acid (propanoic acid)

Butyric acid (butanoic acid)

Salicylic acid

Anthranilic acid

Organic alcohols: Methyl alcohol (methanol)

Ethyl alcohol (ethanol)

Propyl alcohol (*n*-Propanol)

Isopropyl alcohol (isopropanol)

Butyl alcohol (butanol)

Isopentyl alcohol or isoamyl alcohol (isopentanol)

Octyl alcohol (octanol)

Sulfuric acid, concentrated (18 M)

Baking soda, $NaHCO_3$, to neutralize acid spills

Part 2

Acetic acid, concentrated, 17.4 M (glacial)

Ethanol (ethyl alcohol, denatured alcohol)

Sulfuric acid, concentrated (18 M)

Sodium carbonate, $Na_2CO_3 \bullet 10H_2O$, solid

Baking soda, $NaHCO_3$, to neutralize acid spills

Equipment

Part 1

Test tubes, 13×100-mm

Beaker, 250-mL

Beaker, 400-mL

Hot plate or Bunsen burner, ring and wire gauze

Part 2

Erlenmeyer flask, 125-mL

Condenser with cork fittings

Thermometer

Beaker, 400-mL for water bath

Beaker, 100-mL to collect distillate

Separatory funnel or test tube, 15×125-mm, and stopper

Boiling stone

Distilling flask

Clamps

Hot plate, or Bunsen burner, ring and wire gauze

Test tube, 18×150-mm and cork stopper

Capillary dropper

Procedure

> ### Safety Alert
>
> The concentrated sulfuric acid used is very hazardous. Wash spills off yourself immediately with large amounts of water. Neutralize spills on the laboratory bench with baking soda.
>
> The organic acids and alcohols are flammable. Use great care around flames. Do not heat directly with a burner, but use a water bath.
>
> The alcohols are all poisons. Do not ingest them. Methyl alcohol is absorbed through the skin. Wash yourself with soap and water if you spill some on yourself.
>
> A number of the organic acids and alcohols have strong and offensive odors. They may also be skin irritants. Use them in the hood. Wash spills off with large amounts of water.
>
> Never smell a compound by putting it directly under your nose. Instead, hold the compound at least eight inches from your face with one hand, and use your other hand to gently waft the vapors toward your nose.
>
> **Wear Chemical Splash Goggles and a Chemical-Resistant Apron.**

Part 1. Microscale preparation of esters.

1. Prepare a hot water bath.

Fill a 400-mL beaker about half full with water. Heat the water to boiling, and then turn off the flame or the hot plate.

2. Prepare the ester.

Place 10 drops of one of the organic acids in a dry test tube. If using salicylic acid, use a small spatula full, about 0.08 g. Add 10 drops of one of the alcohols. Add 2 drops of concentrated sulfuric acid. Put the test tube into the beaker of hot water and let stand for five minutes.

The odor of the ester is more easily detected when the ester is mixed in some water. Never try to directly smell the ester while it is still hot. Put about 100 mL of water in a 250-mL beaker. Pour the contents of the test tube into the beaker and swirl it to mix the contents. Carefully smell the ester after it is mixed with water by waving some of the vapors toward your nose. Can you identify the odor?

In your laboratory record, give the name and formula of the acid and alcohol used, give the name and formula of the ester produced, and identify the odor of the ester if you can, or describe its odor.

Prepare as many of the esters as your teacher directs.

Part 2. Preparation and purification of ethyl acetate (ethyl ethanoate).

1. Preparation of ethyl acetate.

In a 125-mL Erlenmeyer flask, place 10 mL ethanol, 12 mL glacial acetic acid, 15 drops of concentrated sulfuric acid (18 M), and a boiling stone. Obtain a cork stopper which fits the flask, and bore a hole in it which will accommodate the bottom of a condenser. Cover the cork with aluminum foil, and insert the outlet of the condenser into the cork. The condenser should be clamped in a vertical position, with the bottom of the condenser inside the flask just below the cork. When the condenser is inserted in this manner it acts as a reflux condenser, allowing the vapors of the mixture to condense and return to the reaction vessel. Slowly run cold water through the condenser, in at the bottom and out at the top. Heat the flask in a hot water bath. Raise the temperature of the hot water until the mixture in the Erlenmeyer flask is gently boiling, and continue heating for about 15 minutes. Cool the mixture.

2. **Distillation of ethyl acetate.**

Pour the mixture (including the boiling stone) into a distilling flask and connect the condenser to the side arm of the flask. Insert a thermometer in an aluminum foil-covered cork in the top of the flask with the thermometer bulb even with the side arm of the condenser. Heat the bottom of the distilling flask in a hot water bath until no more distillate is coming over. Record the temperature at which the distillation begins and the temperatures during and at the end of the distillation. Look up the boiling point of ethyl acetate and compare to the distillation temperature.

3. **Separation of the ethyl acetate from alcohol.**

During the distillation some of the unreacted alcohol will distill along with the ethyl acetate. Ethanol is very soluble in a saturated solution of sodium carbonate, while the ethyl acetate is only slightly soluble.

Prepare a saturated solution of sodium carbonate in distilled water by combining 1.5 g $Na_2CO_3 \cdot 10H_2O$ with 5 mL distilled water in a 15×25-mm test tube. Stopper with a cork, shake well and then allow any

HOW TO...

SET UP A DISTILLATION PROCESS

Cooling Water Outlet

Distilling Flask

Condenser

Boiling Stones

Laboratory Burner

Cooling Water Inlet

Receiving Flask

Do not distill to dryness.
Use extreme caution when distilling mixtures containing flammable liquids.
Do not distill liquids with boiling points below 50°C.
Use only cold water in the condenser.
If available, use an electric heating mantle instead of a laboratory burner.

undissolved solid to settle. Pour the clear solution into a separatory funnel, or if none is available, into a second 18×150-mm test tube. Add the distillate, stopper and shake for a minute. If using a separatory funnel, turn it upside down and open the stopcock occasionally to vent the system. If using a test tube, remove the stopper with caution—some pressure may have built up. Separate the two layers. A capillary dropper may be helpful in the separation if you are using a test tube. Measure the mass of the ethyl acetate produced. Pour a little of the ethyl acetate into 200 mL of water and cautiously note its odor.

Disposal

The solutions used to prepare the esters can be safely washed down the sink with a large amount of water according to Flinn Suggested Disposal Method #26b. The ethyl acetate can be saved and used as a solvent, or can be evaporated in the fume hood according to Flinn Suggested Disposal Method #18a. See the appendix of the teacher's manual.

Discussion

In your laboratory report include all of your observations, and answer the following questions:

1. The density of ethanol is 0.79 g/mL. The density of acetic acid is 1.05 g/mL. Assuming that each substance was a pure substance, calculate the moles of each reactant used in part 2. Determine the limiting reactant, and calculate the theoretical yield of ethyl acetate. Use the actual yield to determine the percent yield of product.

2. Why was sulfuric acid added to the mixture of acid and alcohol?

FLINN SCIENTIFIC

LABORATORY NOTES

Preparation of Esters

Preliminary Lab Assignment

Name_____ Date_____ Class_____

1. Explain what an ester is.

2. Draw the structural formula for a carboxylic acid.

3. Draw the structural formula for an alcohol.

4. Write an equation using structural formulas for the reaction of propanoic acid with methanol. Name the product.

5. How is distillation used to purify an ester?